PAPER 00

Introduction to JCT Contracts Discovery

Contents

PAPER 01

Procurement and the contract

Contents

PAPER 02

Contractor selection and tendering

Contents

PAPER 03

Standard forms of main contract and design liability

Contents

PAPER 04

Sub-contractors and specialists

Contents

PAPER 05

Setting up the contract

Contents

PAPER 06

Insurances, bonds and collateral warranties

Contents

PAPER 07

Contract administration: Payment

Contents

PAPER 08

Contract administration: Control of the works

Contents

PAPER 09

Contract administration: Time

Contents

PAPER 10

Contract administration: Termination and insolvency

Contents

PAPER 11

Introduction to dispute resolution

Contents

Paper 00

Introduction to JCT Contracts Discovery

Contents

Overview

1. **Areas Covered**

2. **About JCT**
   2.1 JCT's history
   2.2 JCT's contracts

3. **Recommended reading**

4. **Disclaimer and Interpretation**

Overview

This module is about the understanding and use of JCT construction contracts (a JCT contract is used on the majority of construction projects). A construction contract is the agreement between parties and sets out the rights and obligations of those parties and the position when certain issues under the contract arise.

The module is designed so that it can be adapted by education providers either for use in teaching about JCT contracts as a stand-alone module in its own right, or as part of a broader module on the types of contract and contractual procedures used in the construction industry.

Each section of the module represents a different element of the key areas of the construction contract process which are impacted by JCT's range of construction documentation. As well as explaining the major elements of the JCT suite, the module also aims to explain how JCT contracts are set up and implemented, the various roles of individuals (e.g. contractors, employers, sub-contractors, contract administrators, etc.) within the contract process, and how JCT provisions deal with administrative matters, such as (amongst others) payment, control of the works, and control of time.

The module should be useful to students aiming to gain a comprehensive yet broad understanding of JCT contracts and JCT contractual procedures. The content of the module is produced with the purpose that it supplements a student's knowledge of JCT contracts and helps to explain their contextual use, and is not designed as a replacement to understanding the full details specific to each individual contract.

Paper 00   Introduction

Education providers should benefit from access to JCT content produced 'at source', which provides unique content for use in the development of their courses.

1. Areas covered

The following summary provides a brief overview of the sections covered in this module and the content included under each chapter:

Paper 01 – Procurement and the contract
Construction procurement, contracting strategy, process for selecting the project team, primary project procurement paths and their features, process of selecting an acceptable project procurement path, relationship between information, risk and control, selecting the most appropriate contract for the procurement route.

Paper 02 – Contractor selection and tendering
Process of selecting the contractor, factors affecting contractor selection, pre-qualification, invitation to tender and tender process, tender evaluation, awarding the contract.

Paper 03 – Standard forms of main contract and design liability
Overview of JCT suite of contracts, design within the JCT traditional forms v. design within the JCT Design and Build forms – liabilities and limitations, supporting contract documents.

Paper 04 – Sub-contractors and specialists
The need for sub-contracting, the differences between domestic and named sub-contractors, JCT's sub-contracts and sub-subcontract.

Paper 05 – Setting up the contract
Procedure for completing the contract form (Recitals, Articles and Contract Particulars), information to be considered before completing the form, contract documents, executing the contract.

Paper 06 – Insurances, bonds and collateral warranties
Insurances in construction contracts, major differences between insurance policies, bonds, guarantees and collateral warranties, insurance requirements and options in JCT contracts, the forms of bonds mentioned in JCT contracts, JCT's collateral warranty documents.

Paper 07 – Contract administration: Payment
Payment procedure, basic payment provisions under UK legislation regarding payment for construction works, interim and final payments, loss and expense, relevant clauses of JCT Standard Building Contract (SBC) and Design and Build Contract (DB).

Paper 08 – Contract administration: Control of the works
Roles and responsibilities of those involved in quality control, contract provisions for controlling the works and quality, dealing with defective work (Code of Practice), relevant clauses of JCT SBC and DB.

Paper 09 – Contract administration: Time
Commencement, possession and completion of the works, acceleration, programme, postponement, extensions of time, relevant clauses of JCT contracts.

Paper 10 – Contract administration: Termination and insolvency
Types of insolvency, identifying insolvency, other reasons for termination, consequences of termination, relevant clauses of JCT SBC and DB.

Paper 11 – Introduction to dispute resolution
Major methods of alternative dispute resolution, adjudication under the Scheme for Construction Contracts, dispute resolution under JCT contracts.

2. About JCT

Since 1931 the Joint Contracts Tribunal (JCT) has produced standard forms of construction contract, guidance notes and other standard forms of documentation for use by the construction industry.

Today JCT provides a larger and more comprehensive range of contract documentation than any other contract-producing body in the UK construction industry.

JCT became a Limited Company in 1998 and the organisation is comprised of seven member bodies. The members of the company represent the sectors of the industry who are the key participants (i.e. signatories) in the contract process.

JCT's Members:

- British Property Federation
- Contractors Legal Grp Limited
- Local Government Association
- National Specialist Contractors Council Limited
- Royal Institute of British Architects
- Royal Institution of Chartered Surveyors
- Scottish Building Contract Committee Limited

Each of the member organisations nominate a Director to the Company Board, who sit under the Chair. In addition, The JCT Council contains 47 representatives from its member bodies, who comprise the company's five 'Colleges'. It is through the Colleges that new forms of contract and amendments to existing contracts are produced.

JCT's Colleges:

- Employers, Clients and Local Authorities (British Property Federation, Local Government Association)

- Consultants (Association for Project Management, Chartered Institution of Civil Engineering Surveyors, Royal Institute of British Architects, Royal Institution of Chartered Surveyors)
- Contractors (Contractors Legal Grp Limited)
- Specialists and Sub-contractors (National Specialist Contractors Council Limited)
- Scottish Building Industry (Scottish Building Contract Committee Limited)

2.1 JCT's history

With its formation in 1931, JCT has a long history of setting the standard for contracts in the construction industry.

However, the need for the industry to use standard forms of contract goes back further to the 19th Century. Most building work during this period was procured by approaches that today are described as the traditional or conventional method.

One of the earliest references to a standard building contract appears in *Hudson's Building and Engineering Contracts*, pre-dating JCT and any of its predecessor bodies. But in 1903 a standard form was produced 'under the sanction of the RIBA and in agreement with the Institute of Builders and the National Federation of Building Trades Employers of Great Britain and Northern Ireland'. A revised version of this document appeared in 1909.

In 1931 the Joint Contracts Tribunal (JCT) was formed by the Royal Institute of British Architects (RIBA) and the first JCT standard form of building contract was issued (although the forms were not referred to as JCT until 1977). A local authorities version was published in 1937. Later editions of the JCT contracts were published in 1939, 1963, 1980 and 1998.

In 1963 the range was extended to four, with the publishing of the 'without quantities forms' of the local and private versions.

From 1967 JCT forms were issued and updated via its 11 constituent bodies (reduced to nine when the three Local Authority Associations merged as the Local Government Association). The range of contract families has grown over time, accounting for and adapting to changes in industry practice, new procurement methods, and changes in legislation.

The process of producing standard forms of contract came under review in the Latham Report published in 1994. The report suggested that only those bodies whose members would be a signatory to a form should have the right to approve and authorise its publication. Previously, all new forms and amendments required the agreement of all nine bodies before they could be issued as JCT Forms.

Considering this view, the remaining member bodies decided to operate JCT as a company limited by guarantee and the Joint Contracts Tribunal Limited commenced operation in May 1998.

JCT has subsequently issued the 2005 edition, where the private and local authority versions were combined, and the 2011 edition.

Today JCT is the leading provider of contract documentation, which not only covers standard forms of main and sub-contract for each of the main procurement methods, but also guidance documents, homeowner contracts, partnering documentation, collateral warranties, and agreements.

2.2   JCT's contracts

JCT contracts facilitate the process of constructing buildings. In simple terms, contracts set out the responsibilities and obligations of all parties within the construction process, so it is clear as to what work needs to be done, who is doing it, when they are doing it by, and for how much.

JCT is the UK's leading producer of standard forms of contract, which work on the principle of adapting established benchmark provisions to suit a wide range of projects. A standard form of building contract is a form of contract containing conditions which are applicable, or can be made applicable by the use of alternatives, to a wide range of building projects.

JCT's approach is to produce standard forms that meet clearly defined needs and apportion risk in a way that is appropriate for the procurement methods they reflect. The suite of contracts is made up of 'families' of standard forms, guidance and other documents that are suitable for the majority of construction projects and procurement methods.

JCT contracts are produced to provide two key services:

- Minimise the transaction cost of entering into a contract.
- Provide benchmark provisions in standard form contracts.

There are many reasons why the industry and contract users benefit from the use of standard contracts:

- It saves time.
- It minimises transaction cost.
- It allocates risk in a fair and recognisable way.
- Standard forms are designed in a way that is comprehensive, and cover most of the pitfalls which surround contractual relations in the construction industry.
- Standard forms reflect the benefits that are accrued through precedent – this is achieved by defining benchmark provisions which reflect good practice.
- JCT contracts are developed via a cross-section of the construction industry involved in the contract process. This means that clients (private and public sector), consultants, contractors, specialists, and sub-contractors are all involved in the development of JCT contracts.

3. Recommended reading

The JCT website http://www.jctltd.co.uk provides a valuable resource for further reading including the JCT Practice Note **Deciding on the appropriate JCT contract** (www.jctltd.co.uk/useful-documents.aspx). In addition, JCT provides comprehensive guides to accompany its range of contract documents. Further details can be found at www.jctltd.co.uk/category/guides.

JCT recommends the following additional reading material, which provides a range of guidance to support the following JCT contract documentation:

> *Guide to MW11* by Sarah Lupton (RIBA Publishing)
> *Guide to SBC11* by Sarah Lupton (RIBA Publishing)
> *Guide to IC11* by Sarah Lupton (RIBA Publishing)
> *Guide to DB11* by Sarah Lupton (RIBA Publishing)

4. Disclaimer and Interpretation

This module is intended to provide a resource for the learning and teaching of JCT contracts and contractual procedures. Care has been taken with the production of the module, however it is not designed to replace or replicate the specific terms set out in any of JCT's contract documentation, or as an alternative to professional legal advice. The Joint Contracts Tribunal Limited and its publishers assume no responsibility for any loss or damage caused by any error or omission, whether it is the result of negligence or any other cause.

Unless the context otherwise requires:

- The singular includes the plural and vice versa.
- A gender includes any other gender.
- A reference to a statute, statutory instrument or other subordinate legislation ('legislation') is to such legislation as amended and in force from time to time, including any legislation which re-enacts or consolidates it, with or without modification, and including corresponding legislation in any other relevant part of the United Kingdom.

Paper 01

Procurement and the contract

Contents

Aims

Learning outcomes

1. **Introduction**

2. **Selecting the team**

3. **Procurement routes**
   3.1 Traditional/conventional path
   3.2 Design and Build path
   3.3 Management path
   3.4 Integrated path

4. **Selecting the contract for the procurement route**

Aims

This paper aims to:

- Explain the methods available for contract procurement.
- Review the use and application of JCT standard forms of contract.

Learning outcomes

After studying this paper, you should be able to:

- Describe an acceptable process for selecting the project team.
- Describe the primary project procurement paths and discuss their main features.
- Explain the process of selecting an appropriate project procurement path, discuss the factors which should be taken into account, and explain the relationship between information, risk and control.

This paper provides a broad overview of the major factors influencing construction procurement and contracting strategy.

1. Introduction

The client's first consideration when starting a construction project is to select the project team. Their prior knowledge and experience of contracting will influence them in the initial contact with a consultant and how the team is established. Though procurement decisions, contractual arrangements and tendering procedures are closely interrelated (every project needs a version of each), they involve different considerations and may be linked in almost any combination. Some combinations are more natural and appropriate in certain circumstances than others.

In advising the client on the path they should adopt, decisions are usually made in the following order:

- Identify the project brief, clarify the objectives, understand what the client expects in terms of 'needs' (things the project must deliver) and 'wants' (things which are not essential but which would be nice to have), and prioritise them.
- Decide the procurement approach and overall contractual arrangement.
- Consider what type of contractual relationship is most appropriate (e.g. supplier/customer or some more collaborative arrangement).
- Decide the tendering procedure.
- Select the form of contract.

In the following sections we investigate the factors that influence these decisions.

2. Selecting the team

Selection of the most appropriate team of consultants and contractors is plainly a most important process in achieving project success and must be undertaken with great care. In many cases the 'lead consultant', often a project manager, and architect or engineer will be chosen on the basis of previous experience or personal recommendation, but in the public sector it is common practice for selection to be made on the basis of some kind of competition.

Choice will be based on a range of criteria, including the type, scale, degree of innovation and time frame required for the project, the client's range of experience and expertise, and the skills available in the local market-place. Recent years have seen the emergence of specialist procurement advisers whose role is to guide the inexperienced or lay client through the initial process.

Note also that, for public sector projects let by countries within the European Union, the EU procurement regulations will apply if the anticipated value of the services provided exceeds a pre-set threshold value. These threshold values are set in Euros and are reassessed from time to time. UK Sterling equivalents are published annually by the Treasury, and current values may be found on the UK Government website.

When EU procedures apply, projects must be advertised in the *Official Journal of the European Union* following the defined procedures, and some form of pre-qualification process will generally be required in order to select a manageable tender list from the firms expressing an initial interest.

3. Procurement routes

How a construction project is delivered is determined by the procurement route that is chosen. Procurement is the way resources are brought together to bring about construction works. It comprises the inputs of design, construction and installation, operation and funding: all seen with the various views towards risk.

The most important element in the procurement process is the client because it is their attitude towards risk and their project objectives (which importantly include timing and type of work) and their available funding that will influence the choice of procurement.

The success of a project starts with the project briefing which is dependent upon the client (the person who requires the building or works to be done) and any project adviser that is appointed by the client. The various problems that can arise were identified in *Better Construction Briefing*[i] and the vast majority of these are involved in some way with the procurement decisions.

As the importance of clients' needs became more widely recognised the number of ways of procuring buildings grew in number. Although the number of potential routes is significant, if not infinite (because each project is bespoke in some way), it has been possible to identify characteristics that enable procurement to be classified in terms of a 'procurement system', 'procurement route' or 'procurement path'. These terms are interchangeable and dependent more upon academic considerations as to what constitutes a system, rather than an inherent difference between them. The basic categorisation that is generally accepted is that set out by Masterman[ii].

There are four main procurement paths used in the construction industry, each having its own variations: traditional/conventional, design and build, management, and integrated.

3.1   Traditional/conventional path

The traditional or conventional procurement method has been a standard practice in the construction industry for 150 years, following the emergence of general contracting firms and independent client consultants. There are two main features of the traditional method:

- The design process is separate from the construction (although JCT contracts provide for design of specific parts of the works to be carried out by the contractor).

- Full documentation (i.e. drawings and specification, work schedules or bills of quantities) must be supplied by the client before the contractor can be invited to tender for carrying out the work.

Features of the traditional/conventional procurement method include:

- A contractor is usually selected and appointed by competitive tender, but sometimes by negotiation.
- The terms of many traditional contracts require the client to appoint a professional consultant (e.g. architect, quantity surveyor, contract administrator) to act as an independent contract administrator.
- Full documents are needed for the tendering process – including that from specialist sub-contractors. Time is needed to adequately prepare these.
- The client has control over the design through their appointed consultants (i.e. architect). Generally there is no design responsibility on the contractor.
- Design and construction are separate sequential processes – this can increase the overall time of the project.
- There is reasonable certainty on the cost of the project because the contract figure is usually known at the outset. The contract has provision for cost to be adjusted later in certain defined circumstances.
- Speculative risks are balanced between the parties. A lump sum contract is more in favour of the client whereas a measurement contract is less so. A traditional lump sum approach in terms of design, quality and cost is a relatively low risk procurement option for a client; however, the time required for the project overall is likely to be longer than other procurement methods.

Types of traditional/conventional contract

Lump Sum Contracts

With lump sum contracts, the contract sum is determined before construction work is started. Contracts 'with quantities' are priced on the basis of drawings and firm bills of quantities. 'Without quantities' means a contract priced on the basis of drawings and usually another document, such as a specification or work schedules.

Measurement Contracts

The contract sum for measurement contracts is not finalised until completion of the project, where it is assessed on remeasurement to a previously agreed basis. This type of contract can arise where the works to be carried out by the contractor cannot for good reason be accurately measured before tender. Normally the design will be reasonably complete and an accurate indication of quality will be available to the tenderer. The contract of this type with least risk to the client is probably that based on drawings and approximate quantities. Measurement contracts can also be based on drawings and a schedule of rates or prices. A variant of this is the measured term contract under which individual works can be initiated by instructions as part of a programme of work, and priced according to rates related to the categories of work likely to form part of the programme.

Cost reimbursement Contracts

Sometimes referred to as 'cost-plus' or 'prime cost' contracts, these work on the basis that the sum is calculated from the actual costs of labour, plant and materials, to which an amount is added to cover overheads and profit. The overhead and profit amount can be a fixed-sum, percentage, or some other reimbursement payment. This type of contract is only generally used where the circumstances of the project preclude other alternatives or where a partnering ethos is in place, as it can be quite high risk for the client.

There are two methods in the traditional/conventional route:

- **Sequential method:** Contractors receive complete (or nearly complete) information from consultants on which to base their tenders. The successful contractor then proceeds with the construction of the contract.

- **Accelerated method:** The contractor becomes part of the design team by tendering (either in competition or by negotiation) on partially complete information. In this instance, the successful contractor assists the design team with the completion of the design, etc. and then gets on with the construction process.

One significant problem with the accelerated route is that it is extremely difficult for the contractor to give a lump sum price on partially complete information. Projects of this type are therefore most often let on the basis of some form of cost reimbursement contract, frequently incorporating a pre-set target with the contractor's tender limited to a percentage addition for profit and overheads with perhaps a schedule of rates. It is also common to let contracts of this type on a partnering basis with provisions for incentive payments and 'pain share'.

When time is important, the accelerated traditional system provides a possible answer. It is most likely to be successful if a project office is created in which the whole project team works together. Otherwise the need for speed will prevent the consultants and the contractor from having the time to make well-considered inputs in the right sequence.

Traditional/conventional JCT contracts

Lump Sum Contracts

- Standard Building Contract With Quantities (SBC/Q)
- Standard Building Contract Without Quantities (SBC/XQ)
- Intermediate Building Contract (IC)
- Intermediate Building Contract with contractor's design (ICD)
- Minor Works Building Contract (MW)
- Minor Works Building Contract with contractor's design (MWD)
- Repair and Maintenance Contract (RM)
- Building Contract for a Home Owner with a Consultant (HO/C)
- Building Contract for a Home Owner without a Consultant (HO/B)

- Home Repair and Maintenance Contract (HO/RM)

Measurement Contracts

- Standard Building Contract With Approximate Quantities (SBC/AQ)
- Measured Term Contract (MTC)

Cost reimbursement Contracts

- Prime Cost Building Contract (PCC)

3.2   Design and Build path

Design and Build procurement works on the basis that the main contractor is responsible for undertaking both the design and construction work on a project, for an agreed lump-sum price.

Design and build projects can vary depending on the extent of the contractor's design responsibility and how much initial design is included in the employer's requirements. Nevertheless, the level of design responsibility and input from the contractor is much greater on design and build projects than a traditional contract with a contractor's designed portion.

Adequate time must be allowed to prepare the employer's requirements (the employer usually appoints consultants to facilitate this), as well as time for the contractor to prepare their proposal and tender price. It is vital that the proposal matches all of the employer's requirements before any contract is entered into.

The employer has control over any design elements of the project that are included in their requirements, but once the contract is let, responsibility over design passes to the contractor, so the employer has no direct control over the contractor's detailed design.

The contractor can carry out the design in a number of ways. Often they will appoint their own consultants or use their own in-house team. It is also common practice for the contractor to take on the employer's consultants and continue to use them to complete the detailed design under what is known as a novation agreement.

Features of Design and Build procurement include:

- As design and construction can be carried out in parallel, the overall programme time of design and build projects can be shorter. However this depends on how much design the contractor is responsible for.
- There is reasonable certainty over costs because the contract price is known at the outset. Provided the employer does not order changes during the construction of the work, the contractor will be obliged (subject to the conditions) to complete the project for the contract sum. If the employer does require design or specification changes during the construction period, the contractor advises as to the effect these changes may have on costs or additional time needed.

- Design and Build is a relatively low risk procurement option for the employer, in terms of cost and time. There can be a risk related to design and quality, particularly if the employer's requirements were not properly gathered and if insufficient time went into examining the contractor's proposal.

There are three main variations used:

- **Single entity:** A firm is appointed at the outset to design and construct the project, probably after some preliminary appraisal but without competition.

- **Competitive:** Project documents are produced outlining the client's requirements. Several firms (three to five) may be asked to submit designs and prices, allowing the client a choice in design, price and completion date. For larger projects it would be wasteful of both resources and time for each firm to produce detailed designs at the early stage of the selection process. In such cases the procedure could be in two stages: first, selecting a suitable firm based on outline design/specification details and price; and second, producing an acceptable scheme with the chosen firm.

- **Develop and construct:** Similar to the competitive system, except that a partial or outline design is developed separately, usually through a separate architectural consultancy contract, and each firm tenders on that information. They are then required to develop the outline design into a complete scheme. This method allows the employer to develop the initial design with the aid of a consultant designer, thus helping the client to develop confidence in his scheme, before inviting construction companies to become involved.

Two of the most significant factors affecting the success of a design and build project are:

- **The client's brief (Statement of Employer's Requirements):** It is essential that the client's requirements are identified and stated clearly in the tender documents. These requirements may be detailed, leaving little scope for variation by the competing firms, or broad, leaving maximum scope for development by the firms and allowing maximum buildability. The brief should also include a statement of how the Employer will measure the success of the completed scheme, and of how the tenders will be assessed.

- **Quality control/assurance procedures (QA):** If the client's requirements are broad, it may be best to define them in performance terms. Overall performance may depend on good QA procedures. These should be identified in the brief and cover all stages of the process including design, manufacture and production.

The more the defined requirements can be expressed in terms which are capable of being quantified, the more likely the success of the project is.

Design and Build JCT contracts

- Major Project Construction Contract (MP)
- Design and Build Contract (DB)

3.3 Management path

Management procurement is a method where construction work is completed using a series of separate works or trade contracts which the 'main' contractor is responsible for managing. The main contractor does not actually do the physical work, but is paid a sum for managing the project through the various works packages.

The employer starts by appointing consultants and a contract administrator to prepare drawings, a project specification and cost plan. The employer has control over design throughout the project through their professional team. The contractor is appointed by negotiation or tender, and interview. The works packages are usually let by competitive tender.

It is beneficial for the proposed contractor to be involved as early as possible as they will provide expertise in terms of buildability and programming of the works packages.

Features of management procurement include:

- Design can proceed in parallel with construction, and much of the design might be of a specialist nature related to a specific package of work. Early starts on site are often possible and overall project time can be reduced as a result.
- There is no certainty over cost at the outset and work proceeds on the basis of the cost plan. The final cost of the project will not be known until the final works package is let, however costs can be monitored and controlled by the employer's professional team.
- Design changes are possible during the construction phase, provided that the changes do not affect work on packages already let, which can result in aborted work.
- Completion within the contract period is an obligation of the contractor, and extensions of time cannot be granted without permission from the contract administrator.
- Risk is largely with the employer, in respect of costs and time. A degree of trust and in-house expertise is required for management procurement projects. However this is a low risk option for the employer in terms of design and quality because of the control they have over the professional team.

Management Contracting v. Construction Management

Management procurement generally works on the basis of two different methods:

Management Contracts

With management contracts, the employer appoints a professional team and a management contractor who is responsible for managing the works. The management contractor does not directly undertake any of the construction work. The work is split into packages and carried out by works contractors. The management contractor appoints the works contractors, and they are directly and contractually accountable to the management contractor. A pre-construction phase will allow a programme of works packages to be developed from the drawings, specification and cost plan, which are then let out by competitive tender.

Although contractually responsible for the works contractors, the management contractor is not liable for any default by a works contractor, provided they have complied fully with the terms of the management contract.

A variation on this method is 'design and manage' where the management contractor is responsible for the design team as well as the works contractors.

Construction Management

With construction management contracts, the employer appoints a professional team and enters into an agreement with a construction manager or appoints an in-house manager. The construction manager does not directly undertake any of the construction work. The work is split into packages and carried out by trade contractors. The employer appoints the trade contractors and is directly responsible for them. The construction manager manages the works, but the employer has a major role in directing the project.

Management JCT contracts

- Management Building Contract (MC)
- Management Works Contract (MCWC/A and MCWC/C)
- Management Works Contractor/Employer Agreement (MCWC/E)
- Construction Management Appointment (CM/A)
- Construction Management Trade Contract (CM/TC)

3.4 Integrated path

Integrated procurement, sometimes known as collaborative procurement or partnering, is intended to focus the participants of a project on the mutual objectives of delivering a project on time, to budget and to quality. It is about working as a team, regardless of organisation or location, to meet a client's needs.

The concept of collaborative procurement, where employer and contractor work together to achieve mutually agreed and complementary aims, has origins in high risk ventures such as international oil exploration, where concepts of 'alliancing' have a substantial history. In the UK the long-running arrangement between Bovis and Marks & Spencer for the construction of retail facilities during the 1970s was an early example of the partnering or collaborative approach.

Partnering itself should not be regarded as a procurement system, for two reasons:

- First, rather than being an isolated procurement system, it is a philosophy which can be used in conjunction with most other procurement systems. It is a culture, a mental attitude.
- Second, the principle of 'you scratch my back and I'll scratch yours' is not new. Two partners helping each other for mutual benefit, instead of each one trying to gain the most at the other's expense, has to be the way forward for any civilised business environment. This was identified (not for the first time in a government-sponsored report) in Sir Michael Latham's report *Constructing the Team* (1994).

The potential benefits to the client of successful integrated procurement are:

- Better value for money
- At least the same level of quality
- Less confrontation and therefore speedier delivery
- Less risk, greater certainty of satisfaction
- Fewer claims
- Better communications, understanding and tolerance of problems
- Faster construction
- Continuous improvement

And the benefits to the contractor are:

- Less confrontation
- Greater certainty of workload
- Better communications and understanding from clients
- More involvement in key decision-making
- Greater potential for profit
- Reliable flow of design information

The Integrated process

The prime objective of a collaborative approach is to achieve a project completion in which both parties are satisfied with the result – the so-called 'win-win' scenario.

The process begins with a selection process to establish that all potential partners are suitable in terms of past experience, financial stability, management of resources (human, plant and equipment), competence, and attitude. A successful project requires that client and contractor work together in a spirit of mutual trust and co-operation for the good of the project. This is almost the complete opposite of the confrontational approach, in which contractor and client each tend to look solely to maximising their own advantage. An open and co-operative attitude is therefore vital for the project to succeed.

It may also help if the contractor has experience of working in a collaborative way. Above all, it is particularly important that the key executives of the two organisations not only have a common desire to work together but are able to put this desire into practice.

Initially it may be necessary to invite a selection of contractors to submit tenders and attend carefully planned interviews. A client with an on-going programme of construction works may start with the project-specific integrated approach, hoping that, if successful, it may lead to a strategy of working long-term. A number of contractors have now made collaborative and strategic alliances key features of their business, both at the employer/contractor level and at the contractor/sub-contractor level.

The contractors tendering for a collaborative agreement may be asked to submit details of:

- Past experience
- Human resources
- Equipment resources
- Financial resources
- Procedures for dealing with suppliers and sub-contractors
- Rates and overhead allowances
- Profits

Integrated JCT contracts

- JCT - Constructing Excellence Contract (CE)
- JCT - Constructing Excellence Contract Project Team Agreement (CE/P)

4. Selecting the contract for the procurement route

Procurement and the construction contract are distinct but with overlapping characteristics, the former embracing the latter. A construction contract is vitally important in terms of setting out the rights and obligations, but its impact on the selection of the procurement process should be minimal. The construction contract follows the procurement decision and as such should reflect the relevant aspects of that decision. Consequently, JCT does not produce one contract, but it produces a range of contracts to suit the principal procurement choices and client needs. This decision may or may not involve a pre-construction services agreement, a framework agreement or a consultancy agreement but, with limited exceptions, it always involve a building (construction) contract. Although a contract may be oral (not in writing), good practice dictates that it should be in writing. Otherwise, as a proper record of the agreement is not available, disputes are more likely to arise and, where they do, they are more difficult to resolve.

Once the procurement decision has been made, the appropriate contract or contracts should be determined.

The JCT portfolio not only provides for the general procurement routes but also provides contracts to meet particular aspects of the works, such as minor works, major project works or repair work. When using the JCT portfolio, partnering can be achieved in several ways, e.g. through the use of the JCT - Constructing Excellence Contract, the Partnering Charter (Non-Binding), the pre-construction services agreements or framework agreement used in conjunction with a principal building contract e.g. Standard Building Contract, Design and Build Contract, etc. Most JCT contracts include a provision for collaborative working as well.

So in order to match the contractual framework with the procurement route selected, it is not only necessary to know what contracts are available but also to understand the concept upon which each contract is based. Each JCT contract meets the specific needs of the client and the project; nevertheless there is a large amount of commonality amongst many of those contracts so as to maintain, insofar as one can, the benefits of standardisation[iii].

The principal differences are in the way contracts deal with, for example, design liability, how the price is determined, specialist input, and control of the works. Each JCT contract contains a note on the inside cover as to when it is appropriate to be used and for what type of clients it is suitable. A summary of this information is contained in Paper 03 *Standard forms of main contract and design liability*.

Although a general understanding[iv] may suffice for some purposes in order to understand the precise obligations and procedures or to be able to administer a contract, a detailed knowledge of the contract terms (conditions) is necessary. The primary contract terms are dealt with later in this module.

---

i   *Better Construction Briefing* (1999), Figure 1.1, Peter Barrett and Catherine Stanley, Blackwell.
ii   Masterman, J.W.E (2002) *Introduction to Building Procurement Systems*, Spon Press.
iii   For an understanding of the benefits of standardisation see *The Place of Standard Forms of Building Contract in the 21st Century*, Professor Peter Hibberd, Paper number 120, November 2004 published by the Society of Construction Law.
iv   See the JCT Guides – a guide or guidance note is available for each published contract.

Paper 02

Contractor selection and tendering

Contents

Aim

This paper aims to explain the procedure from a JCT perspective for selecting a contractor for a construction project.

Learning outcomes

After studying this paper you should be able to:

- Describe the process of tendering and appointing a contractor.
- Identify the factors affecting contractor selection.
- Understand the importance of a multi-criterion approach to appraisal.
- Prepare a list of criteria to be used in tender evaluation.

1. Introduction

Selection of the contractor is a fundamentally important part of the procurement process and critical to a project's success. The process of tendering, where a contractor is selected in accordance with a system of set criteria, is a convention that attempts to ensure that the chosen contractor will have the correct combination of technical skills, managerial expertise and financial resources to complete the project in accordance with the employer's requirements.

In modern construction, the selection of a winning tender bid depends on a number of factors. Traditionally, providing all contractors invited to tender meet the employer's requirements, and all tender on the same set of basic information, then the firm submitting the lowest price must represent best value for money. This method posed certain issues, where it became apparent that contractors were prepared to take substantial commercial risks to submit the lowest bid, in order to win the contract. In addition, increasing project complexity, procurement methods and requirements of the employer (particularly with regard to factors such as sustainability) have led to a more complex set of criteria governing the award of contract through the tender process.

In the UK there is a process of three steps for the selection of a main contractor and sub-contractor, which is covered in JCT's Practice Note *Tendering* (to be published in late 2012):

1. The Preliminary Enquiry
2. The Invitation to Tender and Tender
3. Assessment and Award

The principal aspect of tendering is based on the concept of competition. Contractors submit tenders in a bid to win the contract for a project at the maximum level of profit with regard to the competition. They often tender for work at fixed prices, although generally their resource costs are not fixed. Assumptions are made as to the likely plant and labour outputs, which may or may not be achieved, and all the work is generally subject to conditions such as the weather.

In the modern construction environment there are many different types of client and contractor, and commercial relationships between them can take many forms. Traditionally, this takes the form of the supplier/customer arrangement, where the contractor simply provides what the client asks for. In other forms, the relationship is much more collaborative, such as partnering, where employer and contractor work together to develop the project jointly and resolve any issues which may arise.

In the public sector, procurement of construction works is governed by the European Union (EU) regulations, and where the value of a project is over the EU threshold, the project must be advertised in the Official Journal of the European Union (OJEU notice).

Commonly, there are two main types of tendering process that are in use in the industry: single-stage and two-stage. Single-stage tendering (known as 'the restricted procedure' in public procurement) is most appropriate where the design work for the project is sufficiently complete to enable the work to be priced. Two-stage tendering is used for complex projects where the employer's requirements are not finalised and input from the contractor/specialist is needed to achieve this. Two-stage tendering can have an advantage over single-stage, in that parts of the design work and the procurement process are concurrent. They also increase the scope for value engineering.

In single-stage tendering, following the shortlist and tender process, the successful single-stage tenderer is awarded the contract. In two-stage tendering, following the shortlist and tender process, the successful bidder(s) is selected as the preferred contractor, to assist the employer and their professional team in finalising the design in the pre-construction stage and negotiating the final terms of the contract.

Two-stage tendering has for many years been an accepted and encouraged practice in the private sector, but it is not viewed as favourably under the public procurement rules. Whilst the first stage involves competitive tendering, it does not extend to overall pricing of the project in its final form. The procedure is therefore viewed as a negotiated procedure and not as a transparent competitive procedure. In the private sector, however, through establishing appropriate pricing parameters at the tender stage and use of agreements such as the JCT Pre-Construction Services Agreements, it appears in most cases that a sufficient degree of control can be maintained over the final contract price for the procedure to remain a viable option.

2. Pre-qualification

2.1   Selection

Pre-qualification is a process to ensure that, before a tender list is compiled, all interested contractors are assessed to establish that they are equally capable of providing the technical and management expertise and the financial resources to successfully complete the project.

Selection can be carried out as an isolated exercise for each individual project. Depending on the procurement method for a project, all contractors should undergo the same selection process before being included on the tender list.

Alternatively, where a client has an ongoing programme of construction work, they can maintain a standing list of approved contractors. Once a selection process has taken place to compile the list, it would only be necessary to individually screen any new firms not on the list. However, approved lists must be regularly checked to ensure that they remain valid and up to date.

The selection process can apply to main contractors, or used by main contractors to employ their own domestic sub-contractors.

2.2 Procedure

After the preparation of a list of potential contractors, including in public sector projects those who have responded to the OJEU notice, each contractor should be sent a Form of Enquiry letter (model form shown in Figure 02-1). The purpose of the enquiry letter is to establish which contractors are best-suited to the project and who is willing to bid. The letter should be accompanied by a Project Information Schedule (Figure 02-2) and Questionnaire (Figure 02-3).

FIGURE 02-1 JCT Model Form of Enquiry Letter

To: [Insert name and address of contractor.]

Dear   Date:

Project title: Reference No:

Employer:

We are preparing a preliminary list of tenderers for the works described in the enclosed Project Information Schedule. We should be grateful if you would let us know whether you would wish to submit a tender if selected to do so.

Should you wish to be selected, please complete the enclosed pre-qualification Questionnaire and return it to us so as to arrive not later than_____20____.

Assessment of the responses to the Questionnaire will be carried out on the basis referred to in the Information Schedule; we will promptly inform all prospective tenderers whether they have been included in the list of those invited to tender.

This is intended to be [a single-stage/two-stage/competitive dialogue] tendering procedure, conducted in a manner consistent with the JCT Tendering Practice Note (2012 edition). As mentioned in the Information Schedule it is intended that the tender process should be conducted [electronically/in hard copy]. Contract award will be on a [best value/lowest price] basis.

We expect each contractor who now indicates a wish to tender and is then invited to do so to submit a bona fide tender open for acceptance for a period of not less than _____ [days/months].

An indication at this stage that you do not wish to bid will not prejudice you in relation to future projects that we put out to tender. Should you indicate now that you wish to tender but subsequently find that you are unable to do so, please inform us as soon as possible.

The Employer reserves the right to postpone the intended closing date for bids and to accept any tender or no tender at all.

All queries and other communications in connection with the tender process should be directed to

_____ at _____.[1]

---

[1]   Indicate if other arrangements, e.g. for inspection of documents, site visits, etc. are to be made through any other channel.

It is a condition of participation in the process that no participant should at any time prior to notification of the award of the contract disclose to or otherwise discuss with any other tenderer or any third party its actual or intended tender price or any approximation of it.

Yours faithfully

For and on behalf of

[Insert name of issuer and name and position of signatory.]

Enclosures: Project Information Schedule and Annexe(s); Questionnaire

The Project Information Schedule

To encourage a positive response from as many of the listed contractors as possible, the Project Information Schedule should be completed. It must contain sufficient detail so that contractors can decide whether or not to tender, and should include:

- The project and its estimated value.
- The employer, professional team and point of contact.
- The tendering procedure (single- or two-stage) and medium (electronic, hard copy).
- The programme, including anticipated dates for pre-selection interviews, issue of tender documents and tender submission.
- The requirements for contractor's design.
- The JCT contract to be used and any amendments or modifications to the contract form.
- Completed Contract Particulars that show requirements for Collateral Warranties or Third Party Rights, bonds and contractor's insurances (including professional indemnity insurance where there is contractor's design work).
- Any requirements for parent company guarantees or for performance or other bonds that are not covered by the Contract Particulars.
- Mode of execution (as a deed or as a simple contract).
- The basis and criteria for pre-selection, including weightings and order of importance.
- The basis of contract award (lowest price or price and quality), including the criteria for the latter if it applies.
- In relation to error in priced tender documents, whether Alternative 1 or Alternative 2 will apply (see JCT's Practice Note *Tendering* (to be published in late 2012) for details of Alternative 1 and Alternative 2).

FIGURE 02-2 Project Information Schedule

Project Information Schedule

Note: An asterisk* indicates text that is to be deleted or amended as appropriate.

The Project

Project title:

Description of the Works:

Site location:

[site plan attached]*

Client:

Contact address for queries and communications: Contact person(s):
Address:

Tel No:
Fax No:
E-mail:

Estimated cost range: £   to £

Requirements for Contractor's design:[2]

Anticipated starting date of the works:

Anticipated duration of the works:

Access to the Project site, types and location:

Other Employer's requirements or matters affecting the order or methods of working:

Identified risk factors:*

---

[2]   For Design and Build tenders and those involving a Contractor's Designed Portion, it will be necessary to provide additional information, for example on site considerations, planning requirements and any proposed novation of agreements with the professional team. An outline indication should also be given of the extent of design information, etc. likely to be required with tender proposals and any applicable BIM requirements.

Consultants

Names and Addresses of Consultants:

Tel No:
Fax No:
E-mail:

Tel No:
Fax No:
E-mail:

Tel No:
Fax No:
E-mail:

Tel No:
Fax No:
E-mail:

CDM Co-ordinator:

Tel No:
Fax No:
E-mail:

Tendering Procedure

Type of procedure:

Method of submitting documents (electronic/hard copy):

Closing Date for return of questionnaires:

Dates for preliminary interviews, where required:

Basis and criteria of pre-selection of tenderers:

Intended date of issue of tender documents:

Proposed Tender period: weeks

Proposed number of tenderers:

Requirements for alternative tenders and their intended basis:*

The Contract

Form of Contract:[3]

---

[3]   Specify the Contract to be used and its edition/revision. State also if any Amendment and/or Supplement (e.g. for Northern Ireland, the NI Adaptation Schedule) is to apply. (If in a two-stage procedure the successful tenderer will be required in the interim to enter into a JCT Pre-Construction Services Agreement (PCSA) or similar arrangement, that also should be mentioned.)

The Contract Particulars or equivalent items for insertion in the Form of Contract [so far as completed,]* are set out in Annex [   ]* to this Schedule.[4]

Amendments or modifications to the Contract are set out in Annex [   ]* to this Schedule

Particulars of any Listed or Named Sub-Contractors and work intended to be the subject of such sub-contracts:

Details of any required parent company guarantee and, if different from those provided for by the Contract and Contract Particulars, any special bonding arrangements (see Annex [   ]* to this Schedule):

Mode of execution: as a deed/as a simple contract*[5]

Tender Assessment and award

Tenders will be assessed on the basis of lowest price/best value*

The criteria for assessing best value are:[6]*

Price

[List other criteria][6]

Examination and correction of priced bills: Alternative1/Alternatlve2* will apply

Date: _____ 20_____

---

[4] In addition to the general particulars in Part 1 of the Contract Particulars, the Part 2 requirements for collateral warranties/third party rights should be detailed.

[5] Not applicable in Scotland.

[6] If established, specify the criteria for the tender, together with their respective weightings relative to price or their order of importance. If not established, it is sufficient to include them in the Invitation to Tender. Examples of non-price criteria and sub-criteria include:

Approach
- understanding of the requirements
- initiative and team working skills
- method statement and programme
- time requirements (mobilisation period/construction period)

Human Resources
- project management experience and skills
- calibre of designated team
- calibre of management and support staff
- staff training and development

Management procedures
- health and safety
- quality assurance systems
- risk management skills

Sustainability
- environmental policy and record
- proposals for minimising environmental impact
- proposals for systems, materials etc

Design proposals
- aesthetics
- functional requirements
- life cycle costs
- flexibility in use
- maintainability

Technical Capabilities
- record on recent projects
- design capabilities
- BIM experience
- quality inspection capabilities
- facilities

Sub-Contractors and Supply Chain
- selection procedures and quality
- supply chain management
- length of relationships

External relations and community benefit
- community engagement
- job opportunities and training

The Questionnaire

The purpose of the pre-qualification questionnaire is to determine whether the firms chosen to tender for a project have both the necessary technical and managerial skills, and the financial resources to successfully carry out the project.

The questionnaire, which accompanies the form of enquiry letter, is generally divided into four sections:

1. Basic factual particulars.
2. Questions relating to financial matters and good standing – where serious convictions or inadequate resources will automatically disqualify.
3. Regulatory and compliance matters.
4. Technical capacity – capabilities, skills and past performance, which is required to be scored.

For technical capacity, BS 8534 (the British Standard Code of Practice *Construction procurement policies, strategies and procedures*) recommends a weighting for each category so that contractors are judged against an overall capacity threshold.

FIGURE 02-3 Questionnaire

Questionnaire

(This checklist can and should be adapted as necessary, both in terms of format of the questions and the information required regarding contractors' records and capabilities. To the extent appropriate, there should be no requirement for individual prospective contractors to duplicate details covered by their industry standard accreditations. Questionnaires should also avoid details that are unlikely to be evaluated properly at the preliminary stage and can safely be left for checking at a later stage.)

To facilitate assessment of interested Contractors' capabilities and the selection of a tender list for the Project, the Contractor is requested to provide the following information, details and confirmations:

Corporate particulars

- Full company name and registration number
- Principal place of business
- Registered office (if different)
- Contact details for enquiries
- Particulars of ultimate holding company and group structure diagram
- Availability of parent company guarantee, if required
- Relevant trade registrations
- VAT registration number

Financial standing

- Report and audited accounts for last [2/3] financial years
- Statements of turnover for that period in respect of the divisional activities most closely related to the Project
- Contact details for bank references
- Alternative demonstration of financial status (where necessary for a true and fair view)

Technical capability and record

- Recent experience and record on comparable projects and in closely related fields, including (if relevant) team-working and partnering

- Contact details for referees in relation to those projects
- Particular technical skills and capabilities applicable to the Project, including design capabilities (where relevant), facilities, site management, BIM (where required) and quality assurance
- Details of current and anticipated workload and capacity

Management and Personnel

- The Company's management structure and personnel resources and the manner in which they contribute to projects of this type
- The proposed management team for this Project (including names, positions, qualifications, experience and intended roles)
- The Company's policies, procedures, arrangements for ensuring implementation and record in relation to:
  - general training and staff development
  - health and safety matters (including accident rates and safe working/preventive measures, CDM compliance, workforce information and training, occupational health and welfare)
  - environmental management, including operational environmental impact and sustainable construction and operation
  - quality management
  - equal opportunities and diversity
  - community relations and, in public procurement, local economic impact

Insurances

- Details of existing public and employer's liability cover, works insurance, product liability cover and (in cases involving design and/or professional services) professional indemnity insurance (including deductibles/excesses and renewal dates)
- Availability of additional cover specified for particular aspects of the project
- Contact details for contractor's insurance brokers

Sub-Contractors and Supply Chain

- Preliminary plans for sub-contracting and list of preferred sub-contractors
- Selection and quality assurance procedures
- Other supply chain management procedures
- Relationships with major specialists and suppliers

Good standing, material litigation, etc.

- Confirmation that neither the company nor (to the best of its knowledge) any of its past or present directors, officers or persons controlling it or acting as its agent have been charged with or convicted of any offence involving corruption, bribery, fraud, fraudulent trading, theft, money laundering or conspiracy

- Confirmation that there are no material litigation or other proceedings pending or threatened in relation to the conduct of the company's business or arising out of any projects undertaken by the company that involve or may involve the company or which it is aware involves or may involve any member of its supply chain

- Confirmation that there have in the last [3] years been no known breaches of health and safety, CDM, environmental or other statutory regulations relating to its construction activities that have led or may lead to the prosecution of or an order against the company or any of its directors, officers or other employees, or

- if any such confirmation cannot be given, to give brief particulars of the proceedings or matters in question

2.3 Technical factors

Some of the areas covered could include the following:

- **Labour:**
    - Availability of various trades and extent of relevant experience.
    - Size of labour force in relation to current and future work.
    - Level of work subcontracted.

- **Plant:** Similar factors as labour need to be considered.
    - Availability and capacity compared to existing and future commitments.
    - Maintenance facilities.

- **Labour relations:** Rates of pay, labour agreements, previous record of strikes and disputes.

- **Experience with relevant legislation:** Examples might include regulations relating to importation and employment of foreign workers, legislation designed to protect the rights of public sector workers such as the Transfer of Undertakings Protection of Employment (TUPE) Regulations, etc.

- **Management expertise:**
    - Proven management expertise
    - Management structure
    - Lines of communication
    - Management/size ratio

- **Quality assurance and/or environmental compliance:** ISO 9001 or ISO 14001 accredited or working toward accreditation.

- **Relevant experience:** Experience in projects similar to the current scheme showing proven success, and experience working with similar clients under similar contractual arrangements to that proposed for the new scheme.

This is only some of the information that will be required for the technical assessment. For some projects obviously further, more specialised information would be required. For a design and build contract the design capability would also be important.

If this procedure is carried out correctly, then all contractors in the bid list should be technically capable of carrying out the work.

2.4   Financial factors

An assessment of financial matters would typically involve study of the contractor's accounts, balance sheet and directors' reports to assess the company's current financial position over a period of time, typically 3 years.

By calculating a number of financial ratios, it is possible to assess the contractor's ability to take on this contract and successfully complete. The main ratios dealt with are usually:

1. **Acid test ratio:**

   Cash and current debtors
   Current liabilities

   Ideally 1:1

2. **Current ratio:**

   Current assets
   Current liabilities

   Ideally 2:1 because of uncertainty in construction contracts.

3. **Turnover – capital availability:**

   Capital should ideally be turned over six to eight times in a year.

In addition to these, cash position and debt/equity ratio should also be considered.

Furthermore, certain general financial aspects should be looked at, including how much of the contractor's capital would be tied up in this one contract. A study of the actual relationships of the company with other companies would be necessary: i.e. is it a subsidiary of another company?

If this process is carried out satisfactorily, the contractor should be financially capable of carrying the contract through to a successful completion.

Proper records of assessment must be kept so that those not selected for tender can, on request, be properly debriefed. The scoring model and arrangements for pre-selection must be made in advance of the issue of the preliminary enquiries. To minimise the chance of perverse results, the model should be properly tested.

The questionnaire should also make the subsequent assessment of tenders as straightforward as possible. Even in best value or most economically advantageous (MEAT) cases, to the extent that performance against non-price criteria can be properly assessed on the responses to the questionnaire, it is clearly preferable that an assessment is made at that stage.

Under public procurement rules, the assessment of MEAT tenders must be based on MEAT criteria, i.e. (as defined by EU regulations) quality, price, technical merit, aesthetic, functional and environmental characteristics, running costs, cost effectiveness, maintenance and technical assistance arrangements, and (where applicable) the period required for completion.

2.5 Drawing up the tender list

Once the factors to be considered have been decided, it is then necessary to apply a weighting, depending on the relative importance of each of the factors. If safety and one of the criteria from Figure 02-4 were considered the most important aspects, then these would be given a high weighting; completion to time may be considered less important, and this may therefore be given a lower weighting.

The weighting used will need to reflect a number of factors, including:

- The relative importance of price to the employer in the overall evaluation.
- The complexity of the work and the context in which it is to be carried out.
- The type of relationship between the employer and the contractor (e.g. supplier/customer or partner).

Typical price/quality weightings will vary from 15% price/85% quality to 85% price/15% quality.

The qualitative part of the evaluation will then typically be broken down into a number of other factors such as:

- Commercial evaluation
- Technical evaluation

Each member of the selection team acting independently would assess the scores for each contractor against the various factors being considered.

A number of rating systems are used, but the most common ones involve an assessment on a scale of 1–5, 1–10 or 1–100.

A typical 1–10 grading represents the following:

Rating	Rating
Unsatisfactory: falls short of acceptable level	1, 2
Below average: falls below level occasionally	3, 4
Average: acceptable level	5, 6
Above average: meets requirements generally	7, 8
Outstanding: often exceeds requirements	9, 10

An example matrix analysis is shown in Figure 02-4. The contractors obtaining the highest scores would be included in the bid list.

If the contractors have been vetted prior to tendering, all allowed to tender should be capable of carrying out the project to the standard required and have the resources to complete within the contract period.

A further safeguard can be included in the tender documentation requiring the contractor to provide a performance bond. This provides a safety net for the client in the event of non-completion by the contractor (for example, if the contractor goes into liquidation).

In practice, this is a third party guarantee that the contractor will complete the work. If he does not, then the guarantor will reimburse any losses to the employer. Where a contractor is a subsidiary of a larger company, a group or parent company guarantee may be sought.

FIGURE 02-4 Matrix analysis for selection of contractors

Factors or attributes	Weight	Contractor A Rating	Award	Contractor B Rating	Award	Contractor C Rating	Award
Financial stability	20	95	19.0	100	20.0	80	16.0
Management ability	20	100	20.0	95	19.0	95	19.0
On-site supervision	6	90	5.4	100	6.0	90	5.4
Technical expertise	20	80	16.0	100	20.0	90	18.0
Quality of materials	6	95	5.7	95	5.7	100	6.0
Quality of workmanship	10	95	9.5	90	9.0	100	10.0
Quality of industrial relations	4	100	4.0	100	4.0	80	3.2
Safety procedures	4	100	4.0	90	3.6	80	3.2
Keeping to programme	10	100	10.0	100	10.0	95	9.5
TOTALS	100		93.6		97.3		90.1

Contractors are rated out of 100 for each of the factors or attributes, the best for each criterion being given 100 and the marks of the other contractors related to this.

$$\frac{Rating}{100} \times Weight = Award$$

e.g. $\frac{95}{100} \times 20 = 19$

2.6   Number of Tenders

Even with standardised accreditation and pre-qualification procedures, and the use of electronic tendering, preparation of tenders can be costly for all but the simplest of projects. It is important that the number of contractors selected is kept to a realistic minimum. Abortive costs of preparing and evaluating tenders are an overhead cost and an inefficiency that ultimately is carried by the industry and paid for by clients.

Each project or contract needs to be considered in context, but generally it is recommended that for a design and build project, no more than four tenderers should be selected. Where the project is of a lower value, three tenders should be sufficient, and even for projects of a significantly higher value, six would be the maximum.

Where contractors have not been selected to go forward to the tendering stage, they should always be informed promptly and, on request, be provided with appropriately detailed feedback. It is helpful to be able to demonstrate objective assessment of suitability through the ready availability of the scoring matrix for each candidate.

3. The Invitation to Tender and Tender

After a shortlist of tenderers has been drawn up and the other tender documents are available for release (e.g. drawings, Bills of Quantities, specifications, work schedules, together with the employer's requirements), then document packs should be issued or made available to the tenderers with the Invitation to Tender and the Tender Form. (See Figure 02-5 and Figure 02-6.)

Separate tender forms should be provided for each alternative offer sought, and each tender form should identify clearly the offer to which it relates. If tendering is conducted in hard copy rather than electronically, it is good practice to send duplicate documents to each contractor, accompanied by separate envelopes, each with an appropriate identifier, both for each offer that is sought and also for priced documents when they are to accompany the tender.

Before its issue, the employer or designated consultant should complete the Invitation to Tender, indicating:

- The documents included
- The latest time and date for the return of tenders, together with the relevant address or transmission instructions (e.g. email)
- The contact point for any other communications or queries
- The basis of the award and, in best value or MEAT cases, the criteria and weightings to be applied
- The arrangements and procedures with respect to priced documents
- The arrangements for viewing any drawings, details or other information not comprised in the Tender packs
- The person responsible for site visit arrangements

The relevant parts of the Tender Form should also be completed. These include:

- The description and location of the works
- The name and address of the employer
- The name and address of the tendering contractor
- Relevant adjustments to the list of documents
- Particulars of the parent company guarantor (where required)
- The arrangements and procedure regarding the priced documents

FIGURE 02-5 JCT Model Form of Invitation to Tender

Note: An asterisk* indicates text that is to be deleted and/or completed as appropriate.

To:

Project title: Reference No:

Location of the Works:

You are invited to provide a [tender/first-stage tender][7] for the Works as shown and described in the following documents:

- the Drawings listed in the attached schedule;

- the Specification/Work Schedules/Bills of Quantities/Approximate Quantities*;

- the Employer's Requirements*;

- the Outline Construction Phase Plan;

- the following further documents*:[8]

The Works are to be carried out in accordance with the Contract and other conditions specified in the

Project Information Schedule issued with our Preliminary Enquiry dated _____ 20_____ [,

subject to such modifications as are mentioned in the further documents referred to above]*.

Please submit your tender on the attached Tender Form [by transmitting it in accordance with the attached instructions/sealed in the envelope provided] and endorsed with the Project title to

_____ at _____

_____

so as to be received not later than _____ hours on _____ 20_____[9]. Tenders received late will not be considered.

Your tender should be accompanied by the [following further documents, each in the format and completed in accordance with the attached instructions [and each enclosed in the separate envelope(s) provided]:]

- your priced document(s) [and completed Contract Sum Analysis]

---

[7]   The alternative reference to "first-stage" tender relates only to two-stage tender procedures. Where alternative tenders are being sought appropriate adaptations should be made.

[8]   These must for example include the criteria and relative weightings that are to govern the award in best value tendering (if not set out in the original Information Schedule) and should include any revised versions of documents included with the Preliminary Enquiry, any form of parent company guarantee required and (in Design and Build tenders) the required form of Contract Sum Analysis.

[9]   In the case of electronic tendering, the relevant protocol and instructions should be attached or identified. In cases governed by public procurement regulations, there are complex provisions governing the minimum period for submitting tenders.

- [your Contractor's Proposals]*

- [the design/selection and other documents specified [by the Employer's Requirements/in the note

  attached]]*

All queries and other communications in connection with the tender process should be directed to

[_____].[10]

Tenders will be assessed [on the basis of lowest price/against the best value criteria set out [below/in the Project Information Schedule/in the note attached], those criteria having the relative weightings there specified].[11]

You are reminded of the need for confidentiality as set out in the preliminary invitation to tender and your agreement not to divulge your actual or intended tender price or any approximation of it to any other person or body until we notify you of the contract award. At that stage we will supply a list of tenderers (in alphabetical order) which also shows separately the relevant [tender prices/assessed tender scores].[12]

The tendering procedure will be conducted in accordance with the principles set out in the JCT Tendering Practice Note (2012). The Employer reserves the right to postpone the closing date for bids and to accept any tender or no tender at all. No tendering expenses will be payable.

Signed by or on behalf of _____

Signature: _____

Position: _____ Date: _____

FIGURE 02-6 JCT Model Form of Tender

Note: An asterisk* indicates text that is to be deleted and/or completed as appropriate.

Tender for: [Project Title][13]

To: [Employer/Consultant]

From: [Contractor]

We have examined the following documents referred to in the Invitation to Tender:

- the Drawings as there listed;

---

[10] Indicate if other arrangements, e.g. for inspection of documents, site visits etc. are to be made through any other channel.

[11] If for best value tenders the precise criteria weightings have not been given in the Information Schedule, they must be given now.

[12] Where the public procurement rules apply, see regulation 32 of the Public Contracts Regulations 2006 (as amended by the Public Contracts (Amendment) Regulations 2009) for the requirements in relation to Alcatel Letters and debriefing or corresponding provisions of the equivalent Utilities Contracts Regulations.

[13] Where alternative tenders are required a separate form of tender should be used for each tender. The form of tender must indicate clearly the nature of the alternative tender.

- the Specification/Work Schedules/Bills of Quantities/Approximate Quantities;*

- the Employer's Requirements;

- the Contract and the related conditions and modifications;

- the Outline Construction Phase Plan;

- the following further documents:

We offer to carry out the whole of the Works as described in and in accordance with the documents referred to in this Tender for the sum of £ _____ (exclusive of VAT)[14]

*[within [   ] weeks from acceptance of our tender/the Date of Possession,[15] [comprising a period of:

- [   ] weeks from acceptance to the Date of Possession; and

- [   ] weeks from the Date of Possession to the Date for Completion].]

Our fully priced document(s) [and other documents required by the Invitation to Tender, namely

_____]

[is/are attached/enclosed in the separate envelope(s) provided and marked with our name]/We agree to supply our fully priced document(s) upon which the tender is based within 3 days of being required to do so.[16]

We agree that if any obvious errors in pricing or errors in arithmetic are discovered in the priced document(s) before acceptance of this offer, they shall be dealt with in accordance with the Alternative 1/Alternative 2* procedure as described in JCT Tendering Practice Note (2012).[17]

*[For the purposes of the guarantee requirements [set out in the Project Information Schedule] our parent company, namely

_____

(Registered No._____) whose registered office is at_____

_____has confirmed its willingness to execute and deliver to you a guarantee in the specified form.]

We undertake in the event of your acceptance to execute a formal contract with you embodying all the conditions and terms contained in this offer within 21 days of being required to do so by the Employer.

---

[14] In a two-stage tendering process there may be substituted for this paragraph and the remainder of the text (apart from any parent company guarantee confirmation required) a paragraph in terms similar to the following:

"On the basis of the priced document and a first stage tender sum of £ _____ (exclusive of VAT) we offer to enter into second stage negotiations [and a JCT Pre-Construction Services Agreement (PCSA) with you in the agreed form]. Subject to satisfactory completion of those negotiations[, the preparation of priced bills of quantities] and agreement of the contract sum, we confirm our willingness to execute and complete the Works in accordance with the documents and conditions referred to in this Tender."

[15] To be adjusted and completed as appropriate prior to issue to tenderers. Where the contractor can suggest an alternative period, this latter option should in such a case be the subject of a separate tender and tenderers should be supplied with a separate form for the purpose.

[16] These provisions should be conformed with the Invitation to Tender, prior to issue.

[17] Delete whichever Alternative is not applicable, prior to issue, and see the 'Assessment and award' section of the Practice Note.

This tender remains open for acceptance for _____[18] days from the last date fixed for the submission of tenders.

Signed by or on behalf of _____

Signature: _____

Position: _____

Date: _____ 20_____

_____

Note: The completed form of tender [is to be submitted by the means specified in the Invitation

to tender/sealed in the envelope provided] and must be received [by _____

at _____] not later

than _____ hours on the _____ day of _____ 20_____ [16]

3.1   Tender submission

Tenderers should complete the Tender Form and submit it in accordance with the instructions, or where hard copy tenders are required, return them in due time in the envelopes provided. Where priced documents are required to be submitted at the same time, these in hard copy cases should accompany the tender in their separate envelope, marked with the tenderer's name. The period for tendering can be extended, as is stated in the Invitation to Tender, but tenders received out of time should not be considered.

To ensure fair and competitive tendering, it is essential that tenders submitted are based on identical documents and are compliant with them, with no attempt to vary that basis through qualifications in the tenders. If a tenderer considers that any of the tender documents or requirements is deficient or requires clarification, whether technically or in contractual terms, they should inform the employer or the employer's consultant as soon as possible, preferably not less than 10 working days before the closing date for tenders. If it is decided to amend the documents, the employer or consultant should notify all tenderers at the same time and, if necessary, extend the period for tendering.

4. Tender evaluation

Traditionally, tender evaluation is based on price. Provided that tenders have satisfied the criteria of the pre-qualification process, and have submitted tenders based on identical documentation, then the tenderer who has submitted the bid with the lowest tender price will be awarded the contract.

_____

[18] For straightforward, lowest price tendering in cases not involving Contractor's design, 28 days may be sufficient. For best value tenders, Design and Build and other projects involving Contractor's design and/or assessment, longer periods are required. Substantially longer periods of validity are not uncommon and in public procurement cases, sufficient time has also to be allowed for the Standstill Period to elapse before acceptance.

Modern practice, however, is that tenders are evaluated against a range of criteria, including financial issues, technical and commercial considerations and 'cultural fit'. It is a requirement of the EU procurement legislation, and is in any event considered to be good practice, that tender evaluation criteria should be stated in the tender documentation, with a list of the factors and the weightings against each factor to be used in the evaluation.

An examination of the priced documents must take place in order to detect any errors before a tender is accepted. In the case of multi-criteria evaluation, the examination of the priced documents is completed independently of the evaluation of non-price criteria.

If errors are found in the priced documents, the appropriate alternative indicated in the project information schedule will determine how to proceed. This will result either in the tenderer withdrawing or confirming their tender price (Alternative 1), or amending their figure to correct the error (Alternative 2). In the case of withdrawal, or if the amended price is higher than the next lowest bid, then the priced documents of the next lowest tenderer can be examined. The Alternative to be used will be set out in the invitation to tender. Alternative 1 may be inconsistent with a partnering approach and is not considered appropriate in two-stage tendering procedures; Alternative 2 would be more appropriate but is open to abuse if not properly supervised.

With multi-criteria evaluation, each criterion is separately weighted and scored, and all criteria are only brought together at the last stage of the procedure. Sometimes the early part of the evaluation is carried out blind, i.e. not identifying the firm whose bid is being evaluated.

Evaluation will typically comprise:

- A desktop evaluation of the bid submission
- Site visits
- An interview process

4.1   Price

Evaluation of contract price forms part of the desktop process. Several techniques could be used, but the most popular involves comparing the various tender prices and scoring them with a pre-set formula. One popular and simple formula allocates 100 marks to the lowest tender and ranks each alternative according to the percentage difference between it and the lowest. Assuming contractor A submits the lowest price, then the score for any other contractor (n) is calculated as:

$$\text{Score (n)} = 100 - \left\{ \left(\frac{\text{Price (n)} - \text{Price A}}{\text{Price A}} \right) \times 100 \right\}$$

The process may be refined to include comparison with the quantity surveyor's pre-tender statement. In this case the pre-tender estimate could be used as the reference price instead of the lowest tender, or may simply be included as if it were another tender bid.

4.2   Technical evaluation

In evaluating a large contract, various headings may be used to assess the ability to carry through this particular project. These could include:

- management team
- personnel issues
- proposed approach to the work
- work control
- environmental practices and proposed solutions
- productivity
- safety
- quality assurance
- number of subcontractors, perhaps identifying specific firms if important to project
- materials

Each of these criteria may be subdivided and weighted and each category rated by the evaluation team as described in the pre-selection process.

For the management team, for example, important aspects may include qualifications, technical knowledge, length and type of experience, understanding of task, and attitude. This process can be carried out for each factor.

Whatever process is adopted it should have been communicated to tenderers in the invitation to tender: transparency is important and for public sector projects essential.

4.3   Commercial evaluation

This would involve checking the contractual and commercial terms of the tenders and is particularly important on design and build projects where contractors will be offering different solutions.

The assessment can generally be done by a member of the commercial team, but many items to do with design and specification require a technical input.

Both technical and commercial evaluations typically form part of the desktop process, but may also include 'reality checks' from the site visit process.

4.4   Site visits

Site visits should be undertaken as a part of the tender evaluation process, basically to provide a 'reality check' on the contractor's written submission. To be effective, the site visit process needs to be carefully planned, and it is suggested that this is best left to the contractor to do within parameters established by the employer. It is common for site visits to be used also as a reference process for quality, etc., with the standard observed and recorded at the visit being regarded as the minimum which the contractor must achieve in the new scheme.

The contractor should be asked to organise visits to suitable projects both completed and in the course of construction, and to facilitate meetings with previous clients and end users. Such meetings will generally be private, and the contractor will not generally be allowed to participate. The site visit brief should also permit the site visit evaluators to speak in confidence to anyone they meet during the day, including subcontractors, the contractor's own workers, etc.

The evaluation team, which normally will not comprise more than three or four people, needs to be carefully chosen and briefed. Each evaluator should be issued with a pro-forma scoring sheet in order to ensure consistency in the evaluation process. Site visit scores will typically form part of the technical and cultural fit scores.

4.5 The interview

Until recently, contractor interviews have been seen essentially as 'beauty parades' in which the contractor fields his best team, together with a marketing manager and perhaps a main board director.

The process historically consisted of a glossy presentation by the contractor, often in the form of a marketing ploy, followed by a few questions from the panel. Typically the whole process would be completed in an hour or two at most.

Current thinking has reappraised both the function and the form of the contractor interview, particularly in the case of collaborative projects such as partnering. The contractor interview is now seen as a major tool in the evaluation of the contractor's ethical beliefs and business practices, both at the organisational and personal level. It is also used as an opportunity for the client's team to meet the contractor and to assess how well the teams will be able to work together, and for the contractor to assess the client's team. From both points of view, therefore, this has many of the hallmarks of a personal job interview.

In order for this process to be effective:

- The interview must be long enough for the two teams to begin to break down communication barriers – to 'get under each other's skin'.
- Both client and contractor should field the key people who will be responsible for carrying out the project on a daily basis, and who will therefore be responsible for project success.
- The interview panel must be carefully briefed and must agree beforehand on the issues to be addressed.

It is common for the client to set a formal agenda which will be followed for all interviews, and to formulate a formal recording and scoring process to ensure that all interviewees are treated fairly.

The length of the interview will vary depending upon the scale and complexity of the project, but it is likely that at least half a day will be required for each tendering contractor. A typical half-day session might comprise:

- Contractor's presentation, introducing his project team and describing in detail his approach to the work and any perceived problem areas or risks (approx 1–1½ hours).
- Break for refreshments during which the contractor's team and the client's team should be encouraged to meet informally (½–¾ hour).
- Question and discussion session generally led by the panel chair (approx 1–1½ hours).

The above represents the minimum likely to be required for the teams to form a realistic view of each other's capabilities. Where work is more complex, a much longer period may be appropriate. Interviews for one large NHS commission lasted for a whole day with each contractor, during which the teams participated in a range of joint activities, including mini-workshops, discussion groups, etc.

Marks from the interview will contribute to the cultural fit score.

4.6   Cultural fit

With the increase in collaborative working methods, evaluating cultural fit has become important in ensuring that the ethical and commercial values of the contractor and the client are well aligned. Undeniably, there is also a 'human factor' to be considered concerning the relationships between the client and contractor's project teams. Issues to be considered include:

- ethical values of the organisation
- business practices in respect of dealings with other stakeholders
- commercial objectives of the company

An assessment of cultural fit is not necessarily a formal process and depends on a number of factors. This includes the experience of the clients themselves, i.e. whether they are a regular procurer of construction services or a novice or infrequent procurer. An experienced client will have learnt about the types of contractors with whom they fit best and will be better placed to assess newcomers.

Another factor is the degree to which the client is involved in the management of their project, or whether the management and assessment process is more in the hands of the client's advisers. Cultural fit is likely to be more important to the client if they have an active role in the management of the project.

Cultural fit is most commonly assessed at the tender stage and tends to be an informal process addressed through interviews and gathering previous knowledge of the companies involved. At tender stage it is important for the client and their advisers to find out if the people they are dealing with are those who will actively build their project, or if they are just the marketing or some other representative team.

Ultimately cultural fit will involve weighing up a number of factors and will be a judgement on the part of those making the final decision.

4.7 The weightings

It is usual to weight price (quantitative) and non-price (the so-called 'qualitative' factors) in the assessment of the final tender score. The weighting used will be that which is communicated to tenderers at the invitation to tender stage.

In light of the tender document, and having the most up-to-date information, other factors from the pre-qualification process may also be revisited. These might include health and safety record, financial position, cultural fit, etc.

4.8 The award

The technical, commercial, financial and other evaluations will be brought together and a final decision made. Before this is done, however, the total amount of work currently being carried out by each contractor for the client may be considered.

Perhaps the award of this contract to a particular firm would give that firm a very high percentage of work, leaving a difficult negotiating position in discussions for increased costs, or creating a high profile labour situation with possible future problems if a labour dispute arose.

This may seem to be a long, laborious process, but the choice of contractor is generally a critical decision for the successful completion of a contract, and you only get one attempt. It is important that it is correct.

Paper 03

Standard forms of main contract and design liability

Contents

Aim

Learning outcomes

Aim

This paper aims to give an overview of the various standard forms of JCT construction contract in use.

Learning outcomes

After studying this paper you should be able to:

- Explain which form of JCT contract is most appropriate for a given situation
- Identify the features of each form of contract

1. Overview of JCT's standard contract forms

A standard form of building contract is a form of contract containing conditions which are applicable, or can be made applicable, to a wide range of building projects.

JCT's approach is to produce standard forms that meet clearly defined needs and apportion risk in a way that is appropriate for the procurement methods they reflect. The JCT suite of contracts is made up of 'families' of forms that are suitable for the majority of construction projects and procurement methods. JCT contracts are produced to provide two key services:

- Minimise the transaction cost of entering into a contract.
- Provide benchmark provisions in standard form contracts.

There are many reasons why the industry and contract users benefit from the use of standard contracts:

- It saves time.
- It minimises transaction cost.
- It allocates risk in a fair and reasonable way.
- JCT standard forms are designed in a way that is comprehensive, and cover most of the pitfalls which surround contractual relations in the construction industry.
- JCT's forms reflect the benefits that are accrued through precedent. This is achieved by defining benchmark provisions which reflect good practice.
- JCT's contracts are developed via a cross-section of the construction industry involved in the contract process. This means that clients (private and public sector), consultants, contractors, specialists, and sub-contractors are all involved in the development of JCT contracts.

1.1   Standard Building Contract

The JCT Standard Building Contract is designed for large or complex construction projects where detailed contract provisions are needed. Standard Building Contracts are suitable for projects procured via the traditional or conventional method.

Features of projects using the Standard Building Contract:

- The employer is responsible for the design, and this is usually supplied to the contractor by the architect or design team working on the employer's behalf.

However, Standard Building Contracts also have optional provision for a 'Contractor's Designed Portion', if the appointed contractor is to be responsible for the design of specific parts of the works.

- Depending on the type of Standard Building Contract used, the employer (through its advisers) will need to provide drawings and specifications, works schedules or bills of quantities to specify the quantity and quality of work at tender stage.
- Standard Building Contracts are normally administered by a contract administrator and a quantity surveyor.
- Works can be carried out in sections.
- It can be used on both private and public sector projects (see also the *Public Sector Supplement* at www.jctltd.co.uk/public-sector.aspx).
- All versions of the Standard Building Contract can be used with JCT's Pre-Construction Services Agreements (for a general contractor or specialist) and JCT's Framework Agreement.

There are three versions of the Standard Building Contract:

Standard Building Contract With Quantities (SBC/Q)

Under SBC/Q, the employer must provide drawings and bills of quantities to specify the quantity and quality of work. The price and payment structure of the contract is based on a lump sum with monthly interim payments. Sub-contractors can be appointed with written permission of the contract administrator or selected from a list of three names. It also provides for optional named specialist provisions (see the *Named Specialist Update for SBC 2011* at www.jctltd.co.uk/named-specialist-update.aspx). All sub-contractors are domestic and their performance is the responsibility of the contractor. Provisions are included for collaborative working, sustainability, advance payment, bonds (advance payment, off-site materials, retention), third party rights and collateral warranties.

Standard Building Contract Without Quantities (SBC/XQ)

The employer must provide drawings together with a description of works, and either a specification or work schedules at tender stage. The project is generally not complex enough to require bills of quantities. The price and payment structure of the contract is based on a lump sum with monthly interim payments. Other provisions largely mirror those set out in SBC/Q.

Standard Building Contract With Approximate Quantities (SBC/AQ)

Most provisions included in SBC/AQ mirror those set out in the SBC/Q form, but SBC/AQ is used when the employer wants to make an early start for which adequate contract documents cannot be prepared before the tender stage. The employer must provide drawings and approximate bills of quantities. The contractor provides a tender sum which is only an indication of the likely price of the works. The price and payment structure of the contract is based on a tender figure which is converted to a final sum on remeasurement and valuation of all work. Interim payments are monthly.

1.2   Intermediate Building Contract

The JCT Intermediate Building Contract is designed for construction projects involving all the recognised trades and skills of the industry, where fairly detailed contract provisions are needed, but without complex building service installations or other specialist work. Intermediate Building Contracts are suitable for projects procured via the traditional or conventional method.

Features of projects using the Intermediate Building Contract:

- The employer is responsible for the design, and this is usually supplied to the contractor by the architect or design team working on the employer's behalf. If the appointed contractor is to be responsible for designing specific parts of the works, then an Intermediate Building Contract with contractor's design must be used.
- The employer (through its advisers) will also need to provide drawings and bills of quantities, a specification or work schedules to specify the quantity and quality of work at tender stage. When using the Intermediate Building Contract with contractor's design, the employer must also detail the requirements for the parts of the works that the contractor is responsible for designing.
- Intermediate Building Contracts are normally administered by a contract administrator and a quantity surveyor.
- Works can be carried out in sections.
- It can be used on both private and public sector projects (see also the *Public Sector Supplement* at www.jctltd.co.uk/public-sector.aspx).
- Both versions of the Intermediate Building Contract can be used with JCT's Pre-Construction Services Agreements (for a general contractor or specialist) and JCT's Framework Agreement.

As highlighted above, there are two versions of the Intermediate Building Contract:

Intermediate Building Contract (IC)

Under IC, the employer must provide drawings and either bills of quantities, specification or work schedules to specify the quantity and quality of work. The price and payment structure of the contract is based on a lump sum with monthly interim payments. It can be used where provisions are required to cover named specialists. All sub-contractors are domestic and their performance is the responsibility of the contractor. IC includes provisions for collaborative working, sustainability, advance payment, bonds (advance payment, off-site materials) and collateral warranties.

Intermediate Building Contract with contractor's design (ICD)

ICD is used when the appointed contractor is to design specific parts of the works. ICD is similar to IC but additionally provides for a contractor's designed portion. The employer must provide drawings and bills of quantities, a specification or work schedules to specify the quantity and quality of work, as well as detail the requirements for the contractor's designed portion.

1.3   Minor Works Building Contract

The JCT Minor Works Building Contract is designed for smaller, basic construction projects where the work is of a simple nature. Minor Works Building Contracts are suitable for projects procured via the traditional or conventional method.

Features of projects using the Minor Works Building Contract:

- The employer is responsible for the design, and this is usually supplied to the contractor by the architect or design team working on the employer's behalf. If the appointed contractor is to be responsible for designing specific parts of the works, then a Minor Works Building Contract with contractor's design must be used.
- The employer (through its advisers) will also need to provide drawings, a specification or work schedules to specify the quantity and quality of work at tender stage. When using the Minor Works Building Contract with contractor's design, the employer must also detail the requirements for the parts of the works that the contractor is responsible for designing.
- The Minor Works Building Contract is not suitable where the project is complex enough to require bills of quantities, detailed control procedures, or provisions to govern work carried out by named specialists.
- Minor Works Building Contracts are normally administered by a contract administrator.
- It can be used on both private and public sector projects (see also the *Public Sector Supplement* at www.jctltd.co.uk/public-sector.aspx).
- Both versions of the Minor Works Building Contract can be used with JCT's Framework Agreement.

There are two versions of the Minor Works Building Contract:

Minor Works Building Contract (MW)

Under MW, the employer must provide drawings, a specification or work schedules to define the quantity and quality of work. The price and payment structure of the contract is based on a lump sum with monthly interim payments. Provisions are included for collaborative working and sustainability.

Minor Works Building Contract with contractor's design (MWD)

MWD is for use on minor works projects, when the appointed contractor is to design specific parts of the works. MWD is similar to MW, but additionally provides for a contractor's designed portion. The employer must provide drawings, a specification or work schedules to define the quantity and quality of work, as well as the requirements for the contractor's designed portion.

1.4 Major Project Construction Contract

The JCT Major Project Construction Contract is designed for large-scale construction projects where major works are involved. It is used by employers who regularly procure large-scale construction work, and the work is carried out by contractors with the experience and ability to take greater risk than would arise under other JCT contracts. The Major Project Construction Contract is suitable for projects procured via the design and build method.

Features of projects using the Major Project Construction Contract:

- The employer and contractor have their own detailed in-house procedures, so only limited procedures need to be set out in the contract conditions. The contractor assumes more risk than in other JCT contracts. The employer and the contractor, together with their respective advisers and sub-contractors, are experienced in detailed risk management and undertaking large commercial projects.
- The contractor is responsible for the design, as well as completing the works. The scale of design work to be carried out by the contractor can vary. Sometimes the contractor will complete a design based on a concept provided through the employer's advisers. Other instances may call for the contractor to be responsible for producing and completing the design right from the outset, either through their in-house team or employing their own specialist designers.
- Often in Major Projects, a 'novation' agreement is put in place so that the architect or designer who initially worked with the employer continues to complete the design under the responsibility of the main contractor.
- The employer usually employs a representative to exercise their powers and functions under the contract.
- The project can be carried out in sections.
- It can be used on both private and public sector projects (see also the *Public Sector Supplement* at www.jctltd.co.uk/public-sector.aspx).
- The Major Project Construction Contract includes provisions for collaborative working, sustainability and third party rights.
- It can be used with JCT's Pre-Construction Services Agreements (for a general contractor or specialist) and can also be used with JCT's Framework Agreement.

1.5 Design and Build Contract

The JCT Design and Build Contract is designed for construction projects where the contractor carries out both the design and the construction work. Design and build projects can vary in scale, but the Design and Build Contract is generally suitable where detailed provisions are needed.

Features of projects using the Design and Build Contract:

- The scale of design work to be carried out by the contractor can vary greatly on design and build projects. Sometimes the contractor will complete a design based on a concept provided through the employer's advisers. Other instances may call for the contractor to be responsible for producing and completing the design right from the outset, either through their in-house team or employing their own specialist designers.

- The design requirements and responsibility of the contractor in design and build projects go beyond that covered in a traditional contract with a contractor's designed portion. Adequate time and care needs to go in to detailing the employer's requirements so that the obligations of the contractor with regard to the design are clear.
- The employer normally uses an agent (either external consultant or employee) to administer the contract.
- Works can be carried out in sections.
- It can be used on private and public sector projects (see also the *Public Sector Supplement* at www.jctltd.co.uk/public-sector.aspx).
- Under the Design and Build Contract, provisions are included for collaborative working, sustainability, advanced payment, bonds (advance payment, off-site materials, retention), third party rights and collateral warranties.
- The price and payment structure of the contract is based on a lump sum with interim stage or periodic payments.
- It can be used with JCT's Pre-Construction Services Agreements (for a general contractor or specialist) and JCT's Framework Agreement.

1.6 Management Building Contract

The JCT Management Building Contract is designed for construction projects where the employer appoints a management contractor to oversee the works. Construction is completed under a series of separate works contracts. The management contractor appoints the works contractors and manages the project for a fee. Management Building Contracts are suitable for projects procured via the management method.

Features of projects using the Management Building Contract:

- Management Building Contracts are suitable for large-scale projects which require flexibility and an early start on site.
- The employer is responsible for the design, and this is usually supplied to the management contractor by the architect or design team working on the employer's behalf. Often it is not possible to prepare full design information before work begins on site, and much of the design detail may be of a sophisticated or innovative nature involving proprietary systems or components designed by specialists.
- Works under the Management Building Contract are carried out in packages by works contractors and design is often completed in parallel to site activity, which allows for greater flexibility and more control for the employer over design.
- The management contractor employs works contractors to carry out the construction works and the works contractors are directly and contractually accountable to the management contractor.
- Works can be carried out in sections.

Full management contract documentation is comprised of two elements: the Management Building Contract (MC) which is a contract between the employer and the management contractor who will oversee the works; and the Management Works Contract (MCWC/A and MCWC/C) which is a contract between the management contractor and each works contractor who will carry out the work package.

Management Building Contract (MC)

The purpose of MC is for the employer to appoint a management contractor who will then employ works contractors to carry out the construction, and will manage the project for a fee. The management contractor will also administer the conditions. Under the contract, provisions are included for collaborative working, sustainability, third party rights and collateral warranties. The price is based on Prime Cost of the Project plus a fee for the management contractor. MC can be used on both private and public sector projects (see also the *Public Sector Supplement* at www.jctltd.co.uk/public-sector.aspx). MC can also be used with JCT's Pre-Construction Services Agreement (for a specialist) and JCT's Framework Agreement (FA).

Management Works Contract (MCWC/A and MCWC/C)

The Management Works Contract is made up of two parts: the Works Contract Agreement (MCWC/A) which includes the Recitals, Articles and Works Contract Particulars, and the Works Contract Conditions (MCWC/C). It is for use between the management contractor and each works contractor only when the main contract is the Management Building Contract and works contractors are appointed under that contract. It can be used where the works are fully designed, or if the works contractor is required to design all or a part of the works. The Management Works Contract can be used when either the contracted works or the project as a whole is to be carried out in sections. It can be used where the contracted works are to be carried out on the adjustment basis or the complete remeasurement basis. Provisions are included for collaborative working, sustainability, third party rights, collateral warranties and bonds (off-site materials and retention).

1.7   Construction Management Contract

JCT's Construction Management Contract is for use on construction projects where the employer appoints separate trade contracts to carry out the works, and a construction manager to oversee the completion of the works for a fee. Construction Management Contracts are suitable for projects procured via the management method.

Features of projects using the Construction Management Contracts:

- The contract is used where separate contractual responsibility for design, management and construction of the project is desired.
- The employer provides the design and enters into direct separate trade contracts with suppliers to carry out the construction of the works.
- The construction manager is appointed by the employer to manage the project and act as the employer's agent, issuing instructions, making decisions and preparing

certification. The construction manager also administers the conditions of the trade contract.

- Works can be carried out in sections.

Construction Management Contracts comprise two elements: the Construction Management Appointment (CM/A) and the Construction Management Trade Contract (CM/TC).

Construction Management Appointment (CM/A)

This contract is for use between the employer and a construction manager when the construction manager is to manage the project on behalf of the employer. The employer enters into separate direct contracts for the works either using the Construction Management Trade Contract (CM/TC) or a special Trade Contract. CM/A is suitable where separate responsibility for management, design and construction is required. Provisions are included for collaborative working, sustainability, third party rights and collateral warranties. It can be used on both private and public sector projects.

Construction Management Trade Contract (CM/TC)

The Construction Management Trade Contract is for use between the employer and each trade contractor where a construction manager engaged under the Construction Management Appointment (CM/A) is managing the project and administering the conditions of the trade contract. Provisions are included for collaborative working, sustainability, advance payment, bonds (advance payment, off-site materials, retention), third party rights and collateral warranties. The price of the contract is based on a lump sum or remeasurement with interim payments. This contract can be used on private and public sector projects (see also the *Public Sector Supplement* at www.jctltd.co.uk/public-sector.aspx). Works can be carried out in sections. CM/TC can be used with JCT's Pre-Construction Services Agreement (for a general contractor) and JCT's Framework Agreement.

1.8   JCT - Constructing Excellence Contract

In 2006 JCT collaborated with Constructing Excellence to develop the JCT - Constructing Excellence Contract. The JCT - Constructing Excellence Contract can be used to procure a range of construction services and is specifically tailored for use in partnering and where participants wish to engender collaborative and integrated working practices.

Features of projects using the JCT - Constructing Excellence Contract:

- The JCT - Constructing Excellence Contract can be used throughout the supply chain, for the appointment of main contractors, sub-contractors, and consultants. It can be used whether or not the supplier is to design, and the supplier's design input (as either contractor or consultant) can vary.
- The contract expressly underpins collaborative working and the formation of integrated teams when used with the Project Team Agreement, providing for the use of a risk register, risk allocation schedules and performance indicators.

The JCT - Constructing Excellence Contract documents comprise two elements:

<u>JCT - Constructing Excellence Contract (CE)</u>

CE is for use throughout the construction supply chain, and specifically for partnering projects. It can be used whether or not the supplier is to supply the design, and the works can be carried out in sections. Payment provisions are flexible under this contract as either Target Cost option or Lump Sum option can be used. The contract can be used for both private and public sector projects (see also the *Public Sector Supplement* at www.jctltd.co.uk/public-sector.aspx). It can also be used with JCT's Framework Agreement.

<u>JCT - Constructing Excellence Contract Project Team Agreement (CE/P)</u>

CE/P is designed to be used in conjunction with the JCT - Constructing Excellence Contract (CE). The Project Team Agreement is used to formalise the integration of the project team, and includes options that provide for risk and reward sharing arrangements between team members.

1.9   Measured Term Contract

JCT's Measured Term Contract is designed for use by employers who have a regular flow of maintenance, minor works and improvements projects that they would like to be carried out by a single contractor over a specified period of time. The Measured Term Contract is suitable for projects procured via the traditional or conventional method, using a measurement payment structure.

Features of projects using the Measured Term Contract:

- Works are separated into 'Orders' for each separate item and the employer supplies a written description or drawings for each Order where relevant.
- The employer must list the properties to be covered by the contract and state the type of work expected to be covered during its period (the period of the contract is expected to be longer than 12 months but not longer than 36 months).
- The employer must also estimate the total value of the work for the contract period and indicate the minimum and maximum value of any one Order given.
- A contract administrator is normally appointed by the employer to administer the conditions, issue Orders, describe the works and completion dates and certify payments.
- The price of the contract is based on the measurement and valuation of each Order according to the prices in an agreed Schedule of Rates.
- This contract can be used on both public and private sector projects (see also the *Public Sector Supplement* at www.jctltd.co.uk/public-sector.aspx).
- Provisions are included for collaborative working and sustainability.

1.10   Prime Cost Building Contract

JCT's Prime Cost Building Contract is designed for projects that require an early start on site, often for alterations or urgent repair work (such as fire damage). The exact nature and extent of the work is not known until the project is underway, so full design documents are not completed until work has commenced. The Prime Cost Building Contract is suitable for projects procured via the traditional or conventional method, using a cost reimbursement or cost plus payment structure.

Features of projects using the Prime Cost Building Contract:

- The employer is responsible for the design, and supplies a specification describing the work, which may be supplemented with drawings. It is usually not possible to prepare full design information before work begins on site.
- There is a higher risk for the employer in terms of cost. The cost of the project depends on the ability of the contractor to work efficiently and carry out the works as economically as possible. Provisions are included to help keep the expenditure of the Prime Cost to a minimum.
- The contractor is paid the Prime Cost of the works, as well as a contract fee in respect of its non-site overheads and profit. The fee can be a lump sum which is adjusted if the Prime Cost is more or less than that estimated in the contract by a certain percentage. The fee can also be calculated as a 'percentage fee' based on the actual Prime Cost incurred. The fee can also be changed if the employer changes the nature and scope of the works outlined in the Schedules.
- Prime Cost Building Contracts are normally administered by a contract administrator and a quantity surveyor.
- Provisions are included for collaborative working, sustainability, off-site materials bond, third party rights and collateral warranties.
- This contract can be used with JCT's Framework Agreement.
- For use on both private and public sector projects (see also the *Public Sector Supplement* at www.jctltd.co.uk/public-sector.aspx).

1.11   Repair and Maintenance Contract

JCT's Repair and Maintenance Contract is designed for use on individual projects that involve a defined programme of repair and maintenance works to specified buildings or sites. This contract is primarily for use by local authorities and other employers who regularly place small and medium-size contracts for jobbing work and are sufficiently experienced that an independent contract administrator is not required.

Features of projects using the Repair and Maintenance Contract:

- The pricing and payment structure can be flexible, as the employer can seek quotes on the basis of a fixed price, daywork, or other rates, using either a Schedule of Rates or all-in labour rates in a Schedule of Hourly Charges. Payment can be made either by a single payment or by stage payments.

- There is no provision for a contract administrator, so the employer is expected to be experienced in letting contracts for work of this kind and will typically be used to handling contractors' accounts.

The Repair and Maintenance Contract is not suitable for periodic repair and maintenance over a fixed period of time. For this type of work, the Measured Term Contract is more appropriate. It is also not suitable on projects for private home owners.

1.12   Home Owner Contracts

JCT's Home Owner Contracts are designed specifically for consumers and home owners looking for the protection of a contract when appointing consultants or contractors to carry out their building work. They work principally on a basis of giving home owners peace of mind in knowing that the obligations of those they employ – contractors, contract administrators (often architects or surveyors), etc. – are clearly set out and defined.

The Home Owner Contracts are laid out in a simpler way than the rest of the JCT suite. They are written in plain English, with technical and legal jargon deliberately kept to a minimum. Nonetheless, the documents provide for project management, allowing users to record costs and scheduling in one document. They are also used to set out and clarify the work to be done, the price of the work and payment schedule, and factors such as which party will be applying for planning permission, access contractors will have on site, etc. They also provide legal certainty in case any issues should arise.

There are three different versions of the Home Owner Contract:

Building Contract and Consultancy Agreement for a Home Owner/Occupier (HO/C and HO/CA)

This pack of documents is designed for a home owner who has employed a consultant to oversee their building work. It contains both the building contract (HO/C) and the consultancy agreement (HO/CA). The contract is suitable for small domestic building projects such as extensions and alterations. The works are carried out for an agreed lump-sum (including VAT), which can be paid in a single payment on completion, or agreed instalments.

As both the building contract and consultancy agreement are for a residential occupier, they are excluded from the provisions of the Construction Act. However, both documents provide for adjudication in the event of a dispute either between the employer and the contractor, or between the employer and the consultant. The adjudication scheme for the Home Owner Contracts is not the same as adjudication under the Scheme for Construction Contracts.

Building Contract for a Home Owner/Occupier (HO/B)

This contract is for a home owner/occupier who has not appointed a consultant to oversee their work. The employer deals directly with the contractor. Other features of the contract are the same as the HO/C document.

Home Repair and Maintenance Contract (HO/RM)

HO/RM is suitable for small-scale repairs and maintenance of a straightforward nature to domestic buildings. The works are carried out for an agreed lump sum (including VAT), or an hourly rate plus the contractor's invoices for materials. The contract only provides for payment on completion of the works, so the duration of the project should not exceed 4 weeks and would generally be much shorter.

Similar to the other Home Owner Contracts, the HO/RM is a consumer contract for a residential occupier; therefore it is excluded from the provisions of the Construction Act. However the contract does provide for adjudication in the event of a dispute between the home owner and the contractor. The adjudication scheme for HO/RM is not the same as adjudication under the Scheme for Construction Contracts.

2. Supporting and ancillary documents

In addition to the main contracts and sub-contracts, JCT produces a number of documents that provide a number of services. One such service is the provision of the contract guides or guidance notes, which support every main contract and sub-contract. Each guide provides a general introduction to the contract and provides the user with guidance as to how to fill it in.

Other supporting documents JCT provides are the agreement forms. These are used with a range of main and sub-contracts, and cover a range of services, including:

- Appointing specialists, consultants or adjudicators
- Establishing long-term relationships in the procurement of regular work
- Carrying out specific pre-construction services

A summary of the key documents is listed below:

2.1   Consultancy Agreement (Public Sector) (CA)

JCT's Consultancy Agreement is designed for use by public sector employers to appoint a consultant, regardless of discipline, to carry out services in relation to construction works. It can be used with any JCT main contract, with the exception of the JCT - Constructing Excellence Contract (CE), which itself is designed to act also as a form of consultant appointment at any level, and the Home Owner Contracts (HO/C and HO/B).

2.2   Framework Agreement (FA)

JCT's Framework Agreement is designed for use by employers who procure work on a regular basis and want to capture the benefits of long-term relationships within the supply chain. It is also suitable for use where a partnering or collaborative approach is desired on a project.

- It can be used for the procurement of works over a period of time.
- It can be used not only between employers and their contractors/suppliers, but also by contractors, sub-contractors and suppliers who are sub-letting to others in the supply chain.
- It can be used with most standard forms of construction contracts, engineering contracts, or sub-contracts.
- It can be used where compliance with the public procurement rules is required.
- It can be used just on a single project, where engendering a collaborative approach is desired.

2.3   Pre-Construction Services Agreement (General Contractor) (PCSA)

JCT's Pre-Construction Services Agreement (General Contractor) is designed for appointing a contractor to supply pre-construction services under a two-stage tender process. It enables the contractor to collaborate with the employer or their team of consultants to develop detailed designs, to develop the main contract works, or to compile specialist tender documents.

The contractor's involvement at the pre-construction stage is valuable and often essential in the final design process of a project, as well as making preparations for the construction phase, such as the programme, cost plans, buildability and any specialist procurement.

The agreement covers the period from the submission of first stage tenders up to the submission of a definitive second stage tender and entry into a main contract for the construction phase.

The agreement can be used when the main contract is one of the following:

- Standard Building Contract
- Design and Build Contract
- Major Project Construction Contract
- Intermediate Building Contract (with or without contractor's design)

This agreement can be used whether or not the contractor is going to be responsible for any design work. It can also be used where there is novation to the contractor of any specialist sub-contracts, supply contracts, or consultancy agreements.

It is suitable for both private and public sector employers.

With minor adaption, the agreement can also be used for the provision of pre-construction services by trade contractors under Construction Management documentation.

It is not suitable for use between the employer (or main contractor) and specialist sub-contractors (see the Pre-Construction Services Agreement (Specialist) below).

It is not suitable for use with the Management Building Contract.

2.4   Pre-Construction Services Agreement (Specialist) (PCSA/SP)

JCT's Pre-Construction Services Agreement (Specialist) is designed for the appointment of a specialist to supply pre-construction services to either the employer or the main contractor. This document is suitable for substantial and complex projects, the agreement enables a specialist to be involved and give advice prior to the construction phase. The purchaser, assisted by the contractor and relevant specialists, is able to derive the greatest benefit from value engineering exercises at this stage.

The agreement can be used on projects where the main JCT contract is to be one of the following:

- Standard Building Contract
- Design and Build Contract
- Major Project Construction Contract
- Management Building Contract
- Intermediate Building Contract (with or without contractor's design)

and their related sub-contracts are to be used.

It can be used whether or not the specialist is going to be responsible for any design work.

It is suitable where the agreement is between the specialist and the employer, but where the benefit of the specialist's tender may be assigned to the main contractor.

It is suitable for both private and public sector employers.

It is not suitable for use between the employer and a professional consultant. See the Consultancy Agreement (Public Sector) (CA).

3. Communication of design and specification

This section introduces the important concept of communicating design information.

It is standard practice to include contract drawings showing the works. In most JCT contracts based on a traditional procurement method, drawings are prepared by the architect or a consultant whom the architect usually co-ordinates. Design is dealt with differently in the JCT Design and Build forms and in traditional forms.

The extent of the drawings is affected by two considerations:

1. Whether there are bills of quantities (sometimes termed 'contract bills'). These give the quantities of work, so that drawings can be limited to showing the character of the works. The contractor does not have to ascertain the quantities himself by analysing the drawings.

2. Whether the contractor is to perform contract work in developing the design of the architect beyond a particular stage. In these cases the contract drawings are relatively limited in what they show.

If the drawings are to give full information about design and quantities – that is, not being amplified by bills or additional design by the contractor – they must be complete in themselves, not relying on any other source. This is necessary for a lump sum contract such as the Standard Building Contract.

Drawings do not usually state the quality of the works, which is essentially a question of specification. Many of the forms described above allow a separate specification.

There are various ways of indicating the contract sum and how it relates to the designed extent of the works. It may be a sum stated in the articles of agreement or similar document. Or it may relate to an analysis given in another contract document, variously described and differing in nature.

- **Contract bills:** These exist under the Standard Building Contract With Quantities form and are an option under the JCT Intermediate Building Contract.
- **Specification:** This may be presented in a form that allows it to be priced section by section by a series of lump sums.
- **Schedule of activities:** This is a statement of the work to be performed, not in technical detail but in the sections in which it will happen, so corresponding to the programme, again priced as a series of lump sums. In effect it may be identical with the priced specification approach.

3.1 Design within the JCT traditional forms

Traditionally, design was generally thought of as being done by an independent consultant engaged by the employer. Consequently, it was accepted that a contractor was not responsible for the design of the construction and he was responsible for the execution of work and provision of materials only. This is far too simplistic in today's environment and there may be some elements which require design by the contractor or a specialist.

JCT traditional forms deal with the question in the following ways:

1. They provide for a contractor's designed portion. While the overall design remains under the control of an independent consultant, the contractor is to design only part of the works. This is included as an option within all three versions of the Standard Building Contract. A separate 'with contractor's design version' is published for the Intermediate Building Contract and for the Minor Works Building Contract. It is not intended that the contractor's designed portion should extend to the whole of the works because that would conflict with the concept that the independent consultant is to remain responsible for the overall design.

   The contractor's designed portion should be identified at the invitation to tender stage and the employer will have supplied documents showing or describing his requirements for this work. These contracts with the exception of the Minor Works Building Contract with contractor's design (MWD) provide for contractor's proposals in response to the employer's requirements and in these situations the employer indicates that he is satisfied that they appear to meet his requirements.

The exception, in MWD, of not having contractor's proposals is because it is believed that both the limited scale of work envisaged and the likelihood that they will not be prepared, either in time or at all, means that such reference is to be avoided.

2. For specialised installations such as lifts and kitchen equipment, specialists' design becomes a near necessity. The Standard Building Contract provides for optional named specialist provisions (see the *Named Specialist Update for SBC 2011* at www.jctltd.co.uk/named-specialist-update.aspx). As the specialist sub-contractor has no privity of contract with the employer, the JCT Sub-Contractor Collateral Warranty for the Employer will normally be used to introduce collateral responsibility. Under the Intermediate Building Contract, the Intermediate Named Sub-Contract and the Intermediate Named Sub-Contractor/Employer Agreement are provided to cover such situations.

In both approaches it is vital that the elements so designed are physically distinguishable from the rest of the works, which remain as the consultant's design. Separate elements such as structural frame, services installation, etc. are suitable, though even here some interaction with the rest of the building may produce design complications.

3.2   Design within the JCT Design and Build forms

The Design and Build Contract and Major Project Construction Contract make the contractor responsible for the design of the whole works.

In the case of these contracts it is the intention that the contractor takes the employer's requirements and completes whatever design is necessary and submits his proposals.

The Design and Build forms handle design matters as below:

- All the final design under the contract is by the contractor, who may sublet it with consent to outside designers.
- The contractor's design liability is declared to be the same as that of an independent professional designer – that is, one of reasonable skill and care.
- The contract documents are:
    o   the contract itself;
    o   employer's requirements, in effect embodying his brief;
    o   contractor's proposals as a design response to these requirements;
    o   a contract sum analysis as the breakdown of the contract sum into subsidiary sums.
- The employer's requirements are stated in whatever documents (however detailed or minimal) have been put forward by him before or during the tendering process. These are held to indicate to the contractor the essential requirements of the

employer which the contractor has taken into account when preparing his design scheme for inclusion in his tender. In turn, they are held to be properly interpreted by the contractor's proposals. Each document may consist of written or drawn material. There is no formal boundary between them and no contractual definition of what they should contain.

- Where the proposals are incomplete when the contract is formalised, they are to be developed by the contractor post-contractually. They usually require considerable development, as they represent statements of intent sufficient for the employer to make up his mind what the tenderer will provide in outline. No adjustment of the contract sum results from this design development. By implication, the client has a right to object if he considers that the developed design does not come up to the proposals.

- The client has the right to instruct the contractor to change his design – that is, to introduce the equivalent of variations – but not to direct him on how to produce the required effect in detail. The contract sum is adjustable in this case.

- The contractor is responsible for getting any statutory approvals that have not been obtained in advance.

- The contractor is responsible for producing his design in time for construction to proceed to completion without disturbance, subject to any effect caused by the client instructing changes.

Paper 04

Sub-contractors and specialists

Contents

Aims

Learning outcomes

Aims

This paper aims to:

* Explain the various types of sub-contractors used on construction projects.

- Explain the process for appointing them with JCT sub-contracts and the major contractual features of sub-contracting.

Learning outcomes

After studying this paper you should be able to:

- Explain the need for sub-contractors from the point of view of the employer and the main contractor.
- Identify and explain the differences between the various different types of sub-contractors.
- Identify the different types of JCT sub-contract and their use.

1. Introduction

Main contractors require an increasing number of specialists, for two main reasons:

- The increasing use of management contractors and contractors for groups of activities.
- The production process in the construction industry is becoming more complex, and progressively more specialised.

The direct employment of specialist work forces and plant for operations that are not continuous give rise to problems of physical and financial control. To avoid unnecessary costs, contractors tend to restrict themselves to a limited market of the types of work best suited to their permanent labour force and equipment. For other work sections they employ sub-contractors.

The principal advantages of sub-contracting are:

- Specialisation means that the labour and plant employed should be suitable for the task and give increased productivity and quality.
- The main contractor may be able to reduce his supervision and administration costs.

The main disadvantage is the difficulty of programming and control.

2. Types of sub-contractor

Sub-contractors are individuals or firms that enter into a legal contract with the main contractor to complete an agreed part of the contract. JCT's contracts and sub-contracts recognise three types of sub-contractor. These are:

- **Domestic:** The main contractor's own sub-contractors. Domestic sub-contractors may be employed to:
    - Carry out complete packages of work, including design.
    - Construct packages of work designed by others, including provision of all necessary labour, materials and plant.
    - Provide labour only, with all necessary materials and plant provided by the main contractor.

- **Named:** The sub-contractor can be either pre-named in the contract documents or, for provisional sum work, post-named. In the case of pre-naming, the firm must have been selected prior to the main contract tendering. In both cases, the chosen firm becomes a domestic sub-contractor. Provisions for 'naming' sub-contractors are available under the Standard Building Contract, Intermediate Building Contract, Major Project Construction Contract and Design and Build Contract.

- **Listed:** The contractor has a limited choice of a sub-contractor as he must select one of those listed (usually three) in the tender documents for a particular section of work. The eventual contract arrangement is that the chosen firm becomes a domestic sub-contractor. Provision for 'listed' sub-contractors is available in the Standard Building Contract.

3. Legal status

Note that under traditional sub-contracting arrangements in English law, the sub-contract is between the main contractor and the sub-contractor. The Doctrine of Privity of Contract therefore ensures that, since the employer has no contractual link under that contract with a sub-contractor, he can have no direct claim in contract law if the work is found to be defective, unless given by way of a third party right under the Contracts (Rights of Third Parties) Act 1999.

This could leave the employer in a difficult position, particularly where the sub-contract includes elements of design or where it has been broken due to some default (perhaps insolvency) on the part of the main contractor. A separate collateral warranty agreement is therefore widely used on building contracts to provide a direct contractual link between the employer and the sub-contractors, enabling action to be taken in contract law rather than having to rely on attempting to recover damages in tort. JCT, for example, issues the Sub-Contractor Collateral Warranty for the Employer and the Intermediate Named Sub-Contractor and Employer Agreement.

4. Domestic sub-contractors

4.1 Introduction

It is common practice in construction contracts for main contractors to sub-let parts of the work to others. Nonetheless, the main contractor remains wholly responsible to the employer for work carried out by sub-contractors.

There are many reasons why main contractors should want to do this. Some of the most significant might be:

- The work involved is specialised, requiring the use of specialised tools and equipment, specially trained workers or specialised design operatives.
- Sub-contracting allows the contractor to reduce the fixed costs of his business.
- The type of work involved, whilst not particularly specialised, may be something which the contractor only undertakes occasionally, making it uneconomic to keep the necessary skilled labour on their books or to purchase specialist equipment.
- Sub-contracting allows the main contractor to step down some of their risk to the sub-contractors in that, although they remain responsible to the employer, they may be able to pursue the sub-contractor for any costs suffered as a result of defective or late sub-contract work.

4.2 The need for approval

Most standard forms of construction contract attempt to modify the contractor's basic right to sub-let, most commonly by requiring contractors to obtain permission from the appropriate authority (typically architect, contract administrator, project manager, etc.) prior to sub-letting the works.

Standard forms vary in the amount of information which the contractor is required to provide and in the degree of authority vested in those responsible for giving permission. The JCT Standard Building Contract states (clause 3.7) that the contractor should not, without the contract administrator's written consent, sub-contract the whole or any part of the works, and that such consent shall not be unreasonably delayed or withheld. Similar restrictions apply in respect of elements of the design.

Strong reasons are required for withholding permission, and this is especially true if the contractor has based their tender on a particular firm's sub-tender – though this is a risk they take in tendering and the contract administrator is in no way bound by it if he considers a firm to be unsuitable. Proposed domestic sub-contractors are often cleared by the contractor while their tender is still under consideration: although this is not always possible, it is sensible to do so where practicable. The list of sub-contractors is a means of providing a measure of control and of the giving of consent.

4.3   Sub-contract conditions

JCT main contracts set out the minimum conditions required of any sub-contract. These requirements would be met by using the relevant JCT sub-contracts.

For example, the Standard Building Contract and the Intermediate Building Contract require any sub-contract to provide the following:

- If the main contractor's employment is terminated, the sub-contractor's employment is automatically terminated.
- No unfinished materials delivered to the site may be taken away again without the contractor's express approval.
- Where the goods have been paid for by the contractor, title in the goods passes to him.
- Where the employer has paid the main contractor for the goods, title to the goods passes automatically to the employer.
- The sub-contractor must grant the contract administrator a right of access to workshops and other premises as set out in the main contract.
- Each party complies with the CDM Regulations.
- If the contractor fails to pay the sub-contractor on time, then interest becomes due to the sub-contractor under the same terms as those set out in the main contract.
- Any applicable collateral warranties included in the main contract must be provided by the sub-contractor.

5. Named sub-contractors

5.1   Introduction

The process of using named sub-contractors allows the employer to name individual specialists within the contract as domestic sub-contractors to carry out an identified part or parts of the works.

Typical reasons for naming sub-contractors are:

- To ensure that certain specialised or critical parts of the work are carried out by firms of known reliability.
- The work may be a patent form of construction which only one firm is able to undertake.
- It may be necessary to establish contact with certain sub-contractors at an early stage in the design – perhaps before the main contractor has been selected. For example, when the designer wishes to incorporate a specialist form of construction into their design (e.g. a specific form of patented steel or pre-cast concrete frame) or perhaps information on mechanical services which critically affects the production of the working drawings. Of course, this could also be achieved by appointing a consultant.
- Certain materials or specialist components may have long lead times, and may need to be ordered in advance of the main contract being placed.

5.2   Naming of sub-contractors in JCT contracts

Standard Building Contract

The Standard Building Contract provides for optional named specialist provisions (see the *Named Specialist Update for SBC 2011* at www.jctltd.co.uk/named-specialist-update.aspx). By means of appropriate entry in the contract particulars, the employer is able to name individual specialists (who will become domestic sub-contractors) to carry out identified parts of the works. Dependent on the entry selected, the right may be limited solely to specialists pre-named in the contract documents (or their replacement) or, for provisional sum work, may also extend to post-naming.

The contractor has a right of reasonable objection in the case of the naming of any replacement specialist, or if post-naming applies. If he duly notifies such an objection, and also if a named specialist becomes insolvent, there are rights both to an extension of time for resultant delay and to any loss or expense arising, but not where a solvent named specialist is terminated for default, unless the instructions name a replacement.

The modifications included in the Named Specialist Update can be incorporated in two ways, either by amending the contract document itself, or by attaching the update to the contract and inserting a provision within the Articles referring to it. Instructions on incorporating the modifications are included within the update itself.

Intermediate Building Contract

The Intermediate Building Contract provides a framework for part or parts of the works to be carried out by a named sub-contractor, i.e. a person named by the employer or contract administrator who is to be employed by the contractor as his domestic sub-contractor on the basis of the JCT Intermediate Named Sub-Contract Tender & Agreement (ICSub/NAM). The Tender & Agreement is divided into three parts:

- Invitation to Tender (ICSub/NAM/IT)
- Tender (ICSub/NAM/T)
- Agreement (ICSub/NAM/A)

Major Project Construction Contract

This design and build form provides that the employer may require the contractor to appoint a named specialist to design or execute particular work identified in the employer's requirements. The requirements may identify a single named specialist or give a list of suitable specialists. In either case the contractor remains wholly responsible to the employer for the named specialist's performance. The contract also provides for the employer to specify pre-appointed consultants to be novated to the contractor.

The contract contains specific provisions as to the way the contractor is to appoint the appointed consultants and named specialists, and failure to comply with the stated contractual proceedings absolves the employer from liability to pay the contractor for their services. The contract further states that the contractor is solely responsible for the services provided and works carried out by any pre-appointed consultant or named specialist.

Design and Build Contract

The Design and Build Contract includes an optional provision which allows the employer to require that work be carried out only by a sub-contractor named in the employer's requirements but does not give him power to nominate a replacement in any change necessitated by termination of the resultant sub-contract. That can only be done by an instruction that excludes the relevant work from the contract. If the employer wishes the contractor to be responsible for completing that work, the contractor's choice of sub-contractor is subject to his approval, but that is not to be unreasonably delayed or withheld.

6. Types of JCT sub-contracts

6.1   Standard Building Sub-Contract (SBCSub/A and SBCSub/C)

The Standard Building Sub-Contract is made up of two parts: the Sub-Contract Agreement (SBCSub/A) which includes the Recitals, Articles and Sub-Contract Particulars, and the Sub-Contract Conditions (SBCSub/C). It is for use when the main contract is one of the JCT Standard Building Contracts (SBC/Q, SBC/XQ, or SBC/AQ) and where the appointed sub-contractor is not required to design (if design is required then a Standard Building Sub-Contract with sub-contractor's design must be used).

SBCSub can be used when either main contract works or the sub-contract works are to be carried out in sections.

It can be used for sub-contract works that are to be carried out on the basis of an adjusted sub-contract sum (adjustment for variations, etc.) or by complete remeasurement.

Provisions are included for collaborative working, sustainability and bonds (off-site materials and retention).

6.2   Standard Building Sub-Contract with sub-contractor's design (SBCSub/D/A and SBCSub/D/C)

The Standard Building Sub-Contract with sub-contractor's design mirrors the above sub-contract with the exception that it contains provisions for the sub-contractor's designed portion. SBCSub/D is appropriate for when the main contractor is responsible for designing specific elements of the works under the Standard Building Contract, and where the sub-contractor is to design all or parts of the sub-contract works.

6.3 Intermediate Sub-Contract (ICSub/A and ICSub/C)

The Intermediate Sub-Contract is made up of two parts: the Sub-Contract Agreement (ICSub/A), which includes the Recitals, Articles and Sub-Contract Particulars, and the Sub-Contract Conditions (ICSub/C). It is for use when the main contract is either the Intermediate Building Contract (IC) or Intermediate Building Contract with contractor's design (ICD), and where the appointed sub-contractor is not required to design.

ICSub is not suitable if the sub-contractor is 'named' in the main contract: in this case, the Intermediate Named Sub-Contract should be considered.

It can be used when the main contract works or the sub-contract works are to be carried out in sections.

It can be used for sub-contract works that are to be carried out on the basis of an adjusted sub-contract sum (adjustment for variations, etc.) or by complete remeasurement.

Provisions are included for collaborative working, sustainability and off-site materials bond.

6.4 Intermediate Sub-Contract with sub-contractor's design (ICSub/D/A and ICSub/D/C)

The Intermediate Building Sub-Contract with sub-contractor's design mirrors the above contract, with the exception that it is for use specifically when the main contract is the Intermediate Building Contract with contractor's design, and where the appointed sub-contractor is to design part or all of the sub-contract works.

This sub-contract is not suitable if the appointed sub-contractor is 'named' in the main contract: in this case, the Intermediate Named Sub-Contract should be considered.

6.5 Intermediate Named Sub-Contract (ICSub/NAM and ICSub/NAM/C)

The Intermediate Named Sub-Contract is designed for use when the main contract is either the Intermediate Building Contract or the Intermediate Building Contract with contractor's design, and the sub-contractor is 'named' in the main contract whether or not the sub-contract works include design.

The Intermediate Named Sub-Contract is made up of two parts: the Tender and Agreement, which itself comprises three parts in one document (the Invitation to Tender (ICSub/NAM/IT), the Tender (ICSub/NAM/T) and the Agreement (ICSub/NAM/A)), and the Conditions.

It can be used when either the main contract works or the sub-contract works are to be carried out in sections, and for sub-contract works that are to be carried out on the basis of an adjusted sub-contract sum (adjustment for variations, etc.) or by complete remeasurement.

Provisions are included for collaborative working, sustainability and off-site materials bond. The Intermediate Named Sub-Contract is not suitable for any sub-contract work that forms a part of the contractor's designed portion.

Often an Intermediate Named Sub-Contract/Employer Agreement (ICSub/NAM/E) is used in conjunction with the sub-contract when the employer needs to have a direct relationship with the sub-contractor. This is particularly relevant in terms of the design responsibility of the sub-contractor, and if they are required to provide any collateral warranties to any purchasers/tenants or funder of the main contract works.

6.6   Minor Works Sub-Contract with sub-contractor's design (MWSub/D)

The Minor Works Sub-Contract with sub-contractor's design is for use when the main contract is the Minor Works Building Contract with contractor's design, and where the sub-contractor is to design all or a part of the sub-contract works.

It is suitable for a package of work that is straightforward, with a low amount of risk involved. Provisions are included for collaborative working and sustainability. The guidance notes are also contained in the document.

6.7   Major Project Sub-Contract (MPSub)

The Major Project Sub-Contract is for use when the main contract is the Major Project Construction Contract. It is designed to be used where the sub-contract works are fully designed or where the sub-contractor is required to design all or a part of the works.

It can be used when the main contract works or the sub-contract works are to be carried out in sections, and can be used for sub-contract works that are to be carried out on the basis of an adjusted sub-contract sum (adjustment for variations, etc.) or by complete remeasurement.

Provisions are included for collaborative working and sustainability.

6.8   Design and Build Sub-Contract (DBSub/A and DBSub/C)

The Design and Build Sub-Contract is made up of two parts: the Sub-Contract Agreement (DBSub/A) which includes the Recitals, Articles and Sub-Contract Particulars, and the Sub-Contract Conditions (DBSub/C).

It can only be used when the main contract is the Design and Build Contract, and can be used where the sub-contract works are fully designed or where the sub-contractor is required to design all or a part of the works.

It can be used when either the main contract works or the sub-contract works are to be carried out in sections.

It can be used for sub-contract works that are to be carried out on the basis of an adjusted sub-contract sum (adjustment for variations, etc.) or by complete remeasurement.

Provisions are included for collaborative working, sustainability and bonds (off-site materials and retention).

6.9   Short Form of Sub-Contract (ShortSub)

The Short Form of Sub-Contract is for use where a JCT contract is the main contract, and for small-scale sub-contract works that are simple, straightforward and include low risk. It is not suitable if the sub-contract works are of a complex or specialist nature, or if the sub-contractor is required to carry out any design.

It can be used when either the main contract works or the sub-contract works are to be carried out in sections and can be used for sub-contract works that are to be carried out on the basis of an adjusted sub-contract sum (adjustment for variations, etc.) or by complete remeasurement.

It is not suitable where provisions which are fully back-to-back with the main contract are required.

The guidance notes are also contained in the document.

6.10   Sub-subcontract (SubSub)

The Sub-subcontract can be used with any JCT sub-contract where either the sub-subcontract works or sub-contract works are to be carried out in sections.

Sub-subcontract works can be carried out on the basis of an adjusted sub-subcontract sum (e.g. adjusted for variations) or by remeasurement.

It is not suitable where the sub-subcontract works are of a complex technical nature, or if provisions which are fully back-to-back with the sub-contract are required.

The guidance notes are also contained in the document.

Paper 05

Setting up the contract

Contents

Aim

Learning outcomes

1. **Introduction**

2. **The Articles of Agreement**
   2.1 Recitals
   2.2 Articles
   2.3 Contract Particulars
   2.4 Attestation

3. **Conditions of Contract**

4. **Advice and guidance**

5. **Letter of intent**

6. **Amendments to the standard form and qualifications to tender**

Summary

Aim

This paper aims to explain how a JCT contract is established and what should be considered before the start of work.

Learning outcomes

After studying this paper you should be able to:

- Explain the procedure for completing a JCT Standard Building Contract form
- Understand the problems associated with qualifications attached to tenders
- Discuss the importance of establishing a valid contract document

1. Introduction

The parties to a main contract are the employer (client) and the contractor, and the parties to a sub-contract are the main contractor and the sub-contractor.

In order to limit the parties' liability, JCT standard forms include a provision which limits the effect of The Contracts (Rights of Third Parties) Act 1999 only to Third Party Rights of those purchasers, tenants and/or funders identified in the contract by name, class or description of person. JCT standard forms offer Collateral Warranties as an option for the granting of rights to persons who are not a party to the contract.

Therefore, other consultants who appear in the contract documents are not actually parties to the contract and therefore cannot benefit from it directly. For example, a contractor cannot sue the architect **under the contract** because the architect is not a party to the contract and no benefit is intended.

It is important that full details of the requirements for Third Party Rights and Collateral Warranties be given to prospective contractors and sub-contractors in the tender process and be properly incorporated in the contract.

Once a tender has been accepted, it is important that the contract documents are prepared for signature.

As an example, the paper considers a contract let using the JCT 2011 Standard Building Contract (SBC). SBC is published in three versions: With Quantities (Q), Without Quantities (XQ) and With Approximate Quantities (AQ). Specific documentation for other contracts will vary and reference needs to be made to the requirements of each specific form, but the basic principles remain the same.

Contract documents always need to be assembled in their entirety. In the case of a contract let using SBC, they include the Contract Drawings, the Agreement (consisting of Recitals, Articles and Contract Particulars), the Conditions and (in SBC/Q and SBC/AQ) the Contract Bills or (in SBC/XQ) the Priced Document or Specification. If there is a Contractor's Designed Portion, the contract documents also include the Employer's Requirements, Contractor's Proposals and the CDP Analysis.

2. The Articles of Agreement

The Articles of Agreement are made up of the Recitals, Articles, Contract Particulars and Attestation clauses. This part of the contract forms the basis of the agreement between the employer and the contractor, where the contractor agrees to 'carry out and complete the Works in accordance with the Contract Documents' and the employer agrees to pay the contractor the contract sum as adjusted in accordance with the Conditions. The Articles of Agreement contain all those items that require the parties' input by way of specific project details; therefore, they need to be completed carefully and executed by both the employer and the contractor.

2.1 Recitals

The Recitals require insertion of a brief description of the Works, identifiers of the Contract Drawings or of their listing, and if applicable, a brief description of the Contractor's Designed Portion.

The Recitals deal with the following:

- The nature and location of the intended works. (First Recital)
- The Contract Bills, in the form of a fully priced copy of the bills of quantities or approximate quantities provided by the contractor. (Second Recital in SBC/Q and SBC/AQ)
- A priced Activity Schedule where provided by the contractor. (Second Recital in SBC/Q; Third Recital in SBC/XQ) This provision should be deleted if not applicable.
- Identification of the Contract Drawings. (Third Recital in SBC/Q and SBC/AQ; Second Recital in SBC/XQ)
- Pricing Options A (the Priced Document is the Specification or Work Schedules) and B (the Priced Document is the Contract Sum Analysis or Schedule of Rates). (Third Recital in SBC/XQ only)
- The status of the employer for the purposes of the Construction Industry Scheme (CIS) under the Finance Act 2004. (Fourth Recital) CIS sets out the rules for how payments to sub-contractors for construction work must be handled by contractors in the construction industry. Some employers may also count as 'contractors' and fall under the scheme.
- The Information Release Schedule provided by the employer. (Fifth Recital) This schedule states the content and timing of the information to be released by the contract administrator. This provision should be deleted if not applicable.
- Whether the Works are divided into Sections, and the documents containing the description of Sections. (Sixth Recital) This provision should be deleted if not applicable.
- The contract is supplemented by the Framework Agreement identified in the Contract Particulars. (Seventh Recital)
- The Supplemental Provisions identified in the Contract Particulars apply. (Eighth Recital)
- A Contractor's Designed Portion – description, Employer's Requirements, Contractor's Proposals, CDP Analysis. (Ninth to Twelfth Recitals) These provisions should be deleted if not applicable.

2.2 Articles

The Articles outline the primary obligations of parties under the contract and deal with the relevant contractual and statutory appointments and dispute resolution. Articles 1 and 2 form the basis of the agreement – that the contractor shall carry out the works in accordance with the Contract Documents (1), and the employer shall pay the contractor the agreed Contract Sum at the times and manner specified in the Conditions (2).

Articles 3 to 6 are concerned with the contractual and statutory appointments. Article 3 states the appointed Architect/Contract Administrator, Article 4 the Quantity Surveyor, Article 5 the CDM Co-ordinator for the purposes of the Construction (Design and Management) Regulations 2007 and Article 6 the Principal Contractor for the purposes of the CDM Regulations and the Site Waste Management Plans Regulations 2008. In the case of Article 5, this only needs to be completed if the CDM Co-ordinator is someone other than the contract administrator. Likewise, Article 6 only needs to be completed if the Principal Contractor is somebody other than the contractor.

In the case that the project is not notifiable under the CDM Regulations 2007, then Articles 5 and 6 can be deleted.

Articles 7 to 9 deal with dispute resolution. Article 7 refers to Adjudication and care must be taken if SBC is used on a project for a residential occupier. A contract with a residential occupier within the meaning of the Construction Act is excluded and therefore it does not need to contain adjudication provisions, but, unless amendments are made, a residential occupier in entering into SBC will be accepting adjudication as a means of resolving disputes. Clients should be advised accordingly. Article 8 refers to Arbitration, which only applies if the Contract Particulars specifically state that Article 8 and clauses 9.3 to 9.8 apply. Article 9 states that, in the event of legal proceedings, the English courts will have jurisdiction over any dispute between the parties in connection with the contract.

2.3   Contract Particulars

The Contract Particulars contain the project specific information which is referred to in the Recitals, Articles and the Conditions. Entries within the Contract Particulars will need to be deleted to indicate which option applies or, where indicated, additional information should be filled in. In SBC 2011 the Contract Particulars are made of up two parts:

Part 1: General

Figure 05-1 shows a checklist of the key information that should have been considered before completing Part 1 of the Contract Particulars. SBC User Checklist is included in the Standard Building Contract Guide.

FIGURE 05-1 SBC User Checklist for Part 1 of the Contract Particulars

Sections (Sixth Recital)

☐ applicable?

☐ description

Framework Agreement (Seventh Recital)

☐ Is the Contract supplemented by a Framework Agreement?

☐ details (date, title, parties)

Supplemental Provisions (Eighth Recital and Schedule 8)

Collaborative working (Schedule 8, paragraph 1)

☐ applicable?

Health and safety (Schedule 8, paragraph 2)

☐ applicable?

Cost savings and value improvements (Schedule 8, paragraph 3)

☐ applicable?

Sustainable development and environmental considerations (Schedule 8, paragraph 4)

☐ applicable?

Performance Indicators and monitoring (Schedule 8, paragraph 5)

☐ applicable?

Notification and negotiation of disputes (Schedule 8, paragraph 6)

☐ applicable?

☐ name of the Employer's nominee

☐ name of the Contractor's nominee

Contractor's Designed Portion (Ninth Recital)

☐ applicable?

Employer's Requirements (Tenth Recital)

☐ identification

Contractor's Proposals (Eleventh Recital)

☐ identification

CDP Analysis (Eleventh Recital)

☐ identification

CDP: limit of Contractor's liability for loss of use etc. (clause 2·19·3)

☐ amount

Professional Indemnity insurance (clause 6·12)

☐ type, amount, expiry

PI insurance sub-limit: Cover for pollution and contamination claims (clause 6·12)

☐ applicable?

☐ amount

Contract Sum (Article 2 in SBC/Q and SBC/XQ)

☐ amount

CDM Planning Period (clause 1·1)

- ☐ period (days/weeks)
- ☐ commencement/end date

Arbitration (Article 8 and clause 9·4)

- ☐ applicable?
- ☐ appointor of Arbitrator?

Base Date (clause 1·1)

- ☐ date

Date for Completion (clause 1·1)

- ☐ Works: date
- ☐ Sections: date for each Section

Address for service of notices (clause 1·7)

- ☐ Employer
- ☐ Contractor

Date of Possession (clause 2·4)

- ☐ Site: date
- ☐ Sections: date for each Section

Deferment of possession (clause 2·5)

- ☐ applicable?
- ☐ Site: period
- ☐ Sections: period for each Section

Master programme (clause 2·9·1·2)

- ☐ critical paths: applicable?

Liquidated damages (clause 2·32·2)

- ☐ Works: rate and period
- ☐ Sections: rate and period for each Section

Section Sums (clause 2·37)

- ☐ amount for each Section (These must add up to the Contract Sum.)

Rectification Period (clause 2·38)

- ☐ Works: period
- ☐ Sections: period for each Section

Advance payment (clause 4·8)

- ☐ applicable? (Not applicable for Local Authority employer)
- ☐ amount or percentage
- ☐ payment date
- ☐ reimbursement: amount(s) and time(s)
- ☐ Advance Payment Bond: applicable?

Interim payments (clause 4·9·1)

- ☐ first due date

Bond for Listed Items uniquely identified (clause 4·17·4)

- ☐ applicable?
- ☐ amount

Bond for Listed Items not uniquely identified (clause 4·17·5)

- ☐ applicable?
- ☐ amount

Contractor's Retention Bond (clause 4·19)

- ☐ applicable? (Not applicable for Local Authority employer)
- ☐ amount
- ☐ expiry date

Retention Percentage (clause 4·20·1)

- ☐ percentage

Fluctuations Options A, B and C (clause 4·20·1 and Schedule 7)

- ☐ applicable option: A, B or C?

Option A

- ☐ percentage addition (paragraph A·12)

Option B

- ☐ percentage addition (paragraph B·13)

Option C

- ☐ Base Month (rule 3)
- ☐ Non-Adjustable Element (percentage) (rule 3) (For Local Authority employer only)
- ☐ Method of formula adjustment (Section 2 of the Formula Rules: Part I or Part II?) (rules 10 and 30(i)) (Not applicable in SBC/AQ)

Daywork (clause 5·7 in SBC/XQ only)

- ☐ identification of document for Percentage Additions and All-Inclusive Rates

Insurance: Contractor's liability – injury to persons or property (clause 6·4·1·2)

☐ amount

Insurance: Employer's liability (clause 6·5·1)

☐ applicable?

☐ amount

Works Insurance Options A, B and C (clause 6·7 and Schedule 3)

☐ applicable option: A, B or C?

Option A

☐ percentage to cover professional fees

☐ renewal date of annual policy

Option B

☐ percentage to cover professional fees

Option C

☐ percentage to cover professional fees

Terrorism Cover (clause 6·10 and Schedule 3)

☐ details of the required cover

Joint Fire Code (clauses 6·14 and 6·17)

☐ applicable?

☐ Has the insurer specified the Works are a 'Large Project'?

☐ Who is to bear the cost for amendments?

Assignment of rights (clause 7·2)

☐ applicable?

☐ applicable to each Section?

Period of suspension (clause 8·9·2)

☐ period

Period of suspension (clauses 8·11·1·1 to 8·11·1·5)

☐ period

Adjudication (clause 9·2)

☐ Adjudicator's name?

☐ Adjudicator nominating body?

Part 2: Third Party Rights and Collateral Warranties

Part 2 covers the requirements for Third Party Rights and Collateral Warranties. The purchasers, tenants and/or funders should be identified by name, class or description of person. The contractor may be required to grant rights either as Third Party Rights or Collateral Warranties. In the case of sub-contractors, provision is made only for the grant of Collateral Warranties. Not all sub-contractors carry or are able to obtain Professional Indemnity insurance cover, either on a per event basis or at all. Any specified cover levels should be realistic, as should the selection of those sub-contractors from whom collateral warranties may be required.

It is vitally important that the project details are completed with great care. They represent the basis of the work to be carried out and are therefore central to the contract as a whole.

2.4   Attestation

Attestation is where the parties (i.e. employer and contractor) execute the contract with the exchange of signatures or by affixing the company's common seal. Two copies of the contract must be signed by both parties and witnessed as required.

Execution under hand or as a deed

The primary factor governing a decision to execute a contract under hand or as a deed is whether the limitation period for instituting proceedings in contract is to be 6 years, as in the case of execution under hand, or 12 years, where the contract is executed as a deed. The mode of execution of the main contract also determines the mode of execution of any collateral warranties let under it, and the limitation period that applies to both third party rights and collateral warranties.

3. Conditions of Contract

Most standard forms of construction contract separate the general conditions of contract from the project specific data. This is also the case with SBC 2011.

The Conditions of Contract therefore define the rights and obligations of each party for carrying out the work, whereas the details of the *project* (i.e. the work to be carried out, dates, insurance details, etc.) are included in the Articles of Agreement (which includes the Contract Particulars).

The Conditions amongst other things identify:

- The contract documents
- The employer's and contractor's obligations
- The procedures to be followed for controlling the contract, which cover:
    - management of quality of the work

- time
- payments
- changing the works
- assignment and subletting on larger projects
- insurances
- damages for breach of contract
- dispute resolution procedure

The detail and extent of the Conditions of Contract will vary depending on the size and complexity of the project and the method of procurement e.g. traditional, design and build, management, etc. and all contracts are different in terms of form and the style of language used. You should, therefore, read your own contract carefully.

4. Advice and guidance

JCT provides guidance to each main contract and sub-contract either as a separately published guide or as guidance notes. Information about JCT's contracts and guides can be found on the JCT website at http://www.jctltd.co.uk. Each guide provides a general introduction to the contract and provides the user with guidance as to how to fill it in.

In addition JCT also recommends the various Contract Guides authored by Sarah Lupton and published by RIBA Publishing. Information on these texts can be found at http://www.jctltd.co.uk/recommended-reading.aspx.

5. Letter of intent

This is a letter to the contractor notifying him that the client intends to enter into a contract but in the meantime he is authorised to start work. Although this is quite a common practice, particularly on smaller projects, it is not recommended because letters of intent are complex things. How far the letter of intent itself may give rise to contractual obligations is an issue which has often been considered by the courts, particularly where the contract is never entered into. For example, the letter of intent may not be sufficient to indicate what payment will be payable, if any, for work done.

The courts might become involved, again at someone's expense, and the work executed to date may have to be paid on a *quantum meruit* basis ('for what it's worth' – the current value irrespective of any schedules or prices that may have been submitted at tender).

Avoid letters of intent if at all possible.

6. Amendments to the standard form and qualifications to tender

A legally binding contract comes into existence when an offer is made and accepted by the other party. This is why it is important to make sure that tenderers know what contract document is intended to be used and any revisions that may be made to it. The reasons for making amendments to standard forms vary. There may be some amendments which are absolutely necessary to meet particular and essential requirements of the project, but commercial pressures and the desire to change the risk profile are the principal reasons. It is common for employers to make amendments to the standard form, generally in order to place more risk on the contractor.

Whilst it is, of course, the employer's prerogative to do this, practitioners should be very careful to ensure that the amended contract remains workable. The JCT standard forms of building contracts cover benchmark provisions which reflect good practice. The JCT standard forms which are designed for use on large projects, such as SBC, are necessarily complex forms, and clauses are often interrelated. Thus apparently trivial changes may have significant unintended consequences. Amendments should only be made where they are really necessary.

The invitation to tender constitutes an 'invitation to treat'. The tender itself constitutes the contractor's 'offer' to do the work. Unless stated otherwise, the general assumption is that the offer is made in accordance with the conditions set out in the invitation to treat (i.e. the conditions of contract named in it). When the tender submission contains any modifications or qualifications as a condition of their offer, careful consideration should be given to the tender and as to whether it breaches any requirements of the invitation to tender. Where such qualified tenders are accepted, it is essential for the contractor to ensure that the qualifications or modifications are actually made to the Conditions of Contract before signing the contract.

Similarly, from the employer's point of view, it is important to make it clear under what terms a tender is accepted. This is particularly important with sub-contractors' quotations – the tenderer's conditions of trading are often in very small type on the back of an offer. When a contractor sends a letter to a sub-contractor saying: 'We accept your quotation subject to the following conditions', this becomes a counter-offer and needs a subsequent acceptance from the sub-contractor.

Some contractors write qualifications into tender documents or attach them to their tender form. These must be specifically accepted or clearly refuted in any formal acceptance of tender, otherwise they will be deemed to have been accepted. Acceptance can be in many forms: for example, 'by performance', demonstrated by taking delivery of an item.

Note that these issues are particularly important in the case of tenders for projects with a contractor's design or design and build work, where the employer provides a statement of Employer's Requirements to which the contractor responds with a set of Contractor's Proposals. It is easy to see the statement of Employer's Requirements as a kind of specification in which the employer sets out his needs, but this is too simplistic. In a typical plan and specification project the employer is entitled to expect that the contractor will provide what is specified, but in the JCT standard forms (e.g. SBC with contractor's designed portion or the Design and Build Contract), it is the employer's responsibility to examine the Contractor's Proposals to check that they appear to meet their requirements. Where the employer has accepted a divergence from his requirements in the proposals submitted by the contractor, the divergence should be removed by amending the Employer's Requirements before the contract is executed.

It is therefore evident that:

- The statement of Employer's Requirements needs to be complete and unambiguous, whilst still leaving space for the introduction of innovative approaches by the contractor.
- The Contractor's Proposals need to be carefully scrutinised to ensure compliance with the Employer's Requirements before signing the contract.

Summary

The date upon which negotiations between the employer and the contractor are finalised and agreed may mark the point at which the contract comes into existence, and therefore the starting date for the parties' obligations to each other under the contract. Provided that the parties have reached a true consensus on the key terms of the contract (the *consensus ad idem*), the contract may actually be signed much later. However, it is good practice that two identical contracts are prepared and executed by the parties and the effective date (i.e. commencement date of the contract) stated. It is also good practice to execute the contract on or before the effective date. To do otherwise can lead to untold problems.

Each party keeps one original copy of the contract. The contract documents are often locked away and not seen by the contract administrator and quantity surveyor, but it is essential to have available a copy of the contract data and any amendments to the Conditions before starting to manage the post-contract stage of a project.

Having a valid contract that is properly workable depends on the correct information being inserted into the contract form. If there are subsequent problems on a project that lead to a dispute and/or litigation, a properly completed contract clearly demonstrating the intentions of each party is of great importance. It is the starting point from which any dispute can properly be resolved.

Paper 06

Insurances, bonds and collateral warranties

Contents

Aim

Learning outcomes

Aim

The aim of this paper is to provide an overview of the principles and application of the various types of insurance and other protection devices commonly encountered in JCT construction contracts.

Learning outcomes

After studying this paper, you should be able to:

- Identify the various types of insurance and other protection devices commonly included in JCT construction contracts.

- Define and explain the major differences between insurance policies, bonds, guarantees and collateral warranties.
- Explain in detail the insurance requirements of the JCT 2011 Standard Building Contract (SBC).
- Identify the different types of collateral warranty documents used across the JCT suite.

1. Insurance

The major provisions of the JCT contracts regarding indemnities and insurances are included in section 6 – Injury, Damage and Insurance. In SBC, the insurance provisions cover the following areas:

- Injury to persons and property
- Insurance against personal injury and property damage
- Insurance of the Works
- CDP Professional Indemnity Insurance
- Joint Fire Code – compliance

1.1   Injury to persons and property

The contractor is liable for personal injury and for injury or damage to property which arise from the carrying out of the works. The contractor is also to indemnify (i.e. legally protect) the employer against these events.

Under the common law doctrine of vicarious liability, an employer could be held responsible for any injury to people or to property arising out of the carrying out of the works, irrespective of who was to blame. Provisions of JCT contracts protect the employer from any such claims unless the injury is caused directly by himself or by people under his direct control.

The contractor's liability and indemnity are, however, subject to the following qualifications:

- **in respect of personal injury**, the contractor's liability and indemnity excludes injury caused by the employer or people under the employer's direct control or by any statutory undertakers acting in pursuance of their statutory rights and obligations.
- **in respect of damage to property**, the contractor's liability and indemnity is only for the damage arising out of the carrying out of the work and caused by the negligence, breach of statutory duty, omission or default of the contractor or people under his control. The property referred to excludes the works up to practical completion, but it includes sections of the works which are practically complete and the parts taken over by partial possession.

1.2 Insurance against personal injury and property damage

The contractor is required to take out and maintain insurance to cover his liabilities and indemnities. The employer specifies the minimum level of public liabilities cover required in respect of injury to persons or property in the Contract Particulars (clause 6.4), and the contractor is required to provide the employer, on demand, with documentary proof that the required insurance is in place. If the contractor defaults in providing the required insurance, then the employer may take out a suitable policy and (where the cost is included in the contract sum) charge the contractor with the cost.

The contractor's liability in respect of personal injury or death of his employee is covered by the mandatory employer's liability policy that he carries. The contractor's liability in respect of third parties concerning personal injury and property damage is covered by his public liability policy.

There is also provision (clause 6.5) for insurance against non-negligent damage caused by carrying out the works for which the employer may have a liability. Where specifically requested, the contractor takes out the insurance in joint names to protect the employer and the contractor in respect of claims against the employer as a result of loss or damage to any property other than the works due to collapse, subsidence, heave, vibration, weakening or removal of support or lowering of ground water and the like arising out of the carrying out of the works. Cover is to be the amount stated in the Contract Particulars and is subject to the list of exclusions set out in the clause.

The contractor is required to place the policy with insurers approved by the employer and the cost is added to the contract sum.

1.3 Insurance of the Works

There are three optional sets of conditions for the insurance of the works (Options A, B and C, which are set out in Schedule 3). One Option must be chosen in the Contract Particulars. Options A and B relate to the construction of new buildings, and Option C to alterations and extensions to existing buildings.

Option A: New buildings – All Risks Insurance of the works by the contractor; and
Option B: New buildings – All Risks Insurance of the works by the employer

In both cases the person taking out the insurance is required to take out a Joint Names Policy for All Risks Insurance for the full reinstatement value of the works, including professional fees, and to maintain that policy until practical completion of the works. Responsibility after practical completion rests solely with the employer.

There are differences in the administrative arrangements for the two Options, and also differences in respect of the way the cost of the restoration and remedial work is treated. Under Option A (insurance by the contractor), the contractor is not entitled to any payment other than amounts received under the Joint Names Policy in respect of the restoration and remedial work.

Under Option B (insurance by the employer), the restoration and remedial work is treated as a variation, for which the contractor is entitled to be paid.

Option C: Insurance by the employer of existing structures and works in or extensions to existing structures

Option C is relevant where existing structures are involved. The employer is required to take out and maintain both a Joint Names Policy for the full reinstatement cost in respect of damage to the existing structures and their contents by Specified Perils, and a Joint Names Policy for All Risks Insurance for the full reinstatement value of the works plus professional fees. The employer is also required to maintain that policy until practical completion. Any restoration and remedial work required is treated as a variation, for which the contractor is entitled to be paid.

Option C does, however, recognise that substantial damage to the existing structure may mean that the project may be rendered no longer viable, and it therefore permits either party to terminate the contractor's employment 'if it is just and equitable to do so'.

The term 'Joint Names Policy', and other relevant insurance terms, are defined in clause 6.8. The policy (or policies) are required to include the employer and the contractor as composite insured and to provide that the insurer has no right of recourse against either of them, irrespective of which party claims under the policy or may otherwise have been liable for the loss or damage. By clause 6.9, the Joint Names Policy for the works is also required either to recognise each sub-contractor as an insured or to include a waiver of rights of subrogation against him in respect of loss or damage caused by the Specified Perils.

'All Risks Insurance' as a defined term has a meaning somewhat narrower than the phrase 'all risks' might otherwise imply. Briefly, the policy is to cover physical loss or damage to work executed or site materials (but not the contractor's plant and equipment), and it will usually exclude loss or damage caused by wear and tear/deterioration, defects in design or workmanship, war or Excepted Risks and also inventory losses that are not traceable to an identified event. However, it is not entirely straightforward and requires the 'buy back' of Terrorism Cover. In the case of Terrorism Cover (clause 6.10), where the extension of cover will involve an additional premium and may in certain situations be difficult to effect, the requirement is now expressly limited to Pool Re Cover or such other cover as is agreed and set out in the Contract Particulars. That extension and any other relevant details of works insurance require discussion and agreement between the parties and their insurance advisers prior to entering into the contract. If a party is notified by the insurers of a change in the availability of the Terrorism Cover, he should immediately notify the other party. In accordance with clause 6.11, the employer should then inform whether he wishes the contractor to continue with the works or to terminate the contractor's employment.

Difficulty can also arise in relation to joint names insurance of existing structures, particularly in cases that involve residential owner-occupiers or leaseholders whose insurance is effected by their landlord. (In the case of leaseholders, this often arises with work in blocks of flats and also arises with commercial premises, e.g. on fitting-out contracts.) A solution in certain cases may be to use Option A (or possibly Option B) in respect of the works and site materials, with the employer continuing separately with cover in his sole name for his own risk in respect of loss or damage to the existing structures and contents, and with the contractor covering his risk in respect of such loss and damage through his Public Liability policy under clause 6.4. There are, however, further complications where the employer is only one of several leaseholders in the building who might be affected and the contractor has difficulty in obtaining public liability cover in an appropriate amount. In such cases, prior to entering into the contract, not only must the employer inform the existing structure and contents insurers of the intention to carry out the work, but professional insurance advice must be sought on appropriate structuring of cover, cover levels and the consequential amendments to the contract that may be needed.

1.4 CDP Professional Indemnity Insurance

Where the work contains a contractor's designed portion (CDP) the contractor is required to take out a Professional Indemnity policy as stated in the Contract Particulars. The contractor is required to maintain the policy until the expiry date specified in the Contract Particulars, provided it remains available at reasonable rates. If the insurance ceases to be available at reasonable rates then the contractor must notify the employer, and the contractor and the employer are then required to discuss how best the employer and the contractor may be protected.

1.5 Joint Fire Code – compliance

The Joint Fire Code, i.e. *The Joint Code of Practice on the Protection from Fire of Construction Sites and Buildings Undergoing Renovation* published by the Construction Confederation and the Fire Protection Association, is a voluntary code designed to reduce the incidence of fire on construction sites.

The Joint Fire Code is generally required by insurers to apply and, if stated to apply in the Contract Particulars, both the employer and the contractor are bound to comply with its requirements and the other provisions of clauses 6.15 and 6.16, and they need to make sure that others employed by them also comply. In the event of a breach of the Code, the contractor is to ensure that any remedial measure required by the insurer are carried out and, if he fails to do so, the employer may employ others for the purpose.

Where the remedial measures require a variation to the works, the contract administrator must issue the required variation and the contractor will be paid for such variation. Where no variation is required, the contractor is required to carry out the necessary work at his own cost within a specified time.

If the Joint Fire Code is amended after the Base Date, any costs incurred in complying with the revised Code are paid by the party as specified in the Contract Particulars.

2. Bonds and guarantees

Despite a comprehensive tendering process and careful evaluation and selection, there is always concern that a contractor may go into liquidation before completing the contract work, leaving the employer in a difficult situation. Although there will be the retention monies, these may not be sufficient to retrieve the situation. It is therefore increasingly common for additional protection to be sought, in the form of either a bond or a guarantee.

2.1 Bonds

In general terms a bond is an undertaking by one party, known as a surety or guarantor, addressed to another party, known as the beneficiary or owner, to do or to refrain from doing certain things. The contractor in this arrangement is known as the principal. In the construction industry, bonds commonly take the form of the surety (a bank/insurer) promising to make payment to the employer should the contractor default on his obligations under the contract. The amount of money guaranteed by the bond will vary according to its type.

JCT contracts contain the forms of bonds referred to in the contract in a schedule and they are also available to download from the JCT website (www.jctltd.co.uk/useful-documents.aspx). For example, Schedule 6 of SBC includes the three forms of bonds:

- Advance Payment Bond
- Bond in respect of payment for off-site materials and/or goods: This relates to Listed Items
- Retention Bond

The Contract Particulars should state whether any of the above bonds are required and include the related details.

An Advance Payment Bond is normally used where the employer and the contractor agree to operate the advance payment provisions (clause 4.8) and where the employer sees a benefit in assisting the contractor's cash flow. A bond in respect of payments for off-site materials and/or goods is used where the employer has agreed that the Listed Items (clause 4.17) can be paid for before they are delivered to the site. A retention bond is given by the contractor as an alternative to the deduction of retention.

Other types of bond such as performance bonds could be considered. Performance bonds allow the employer to recover monies which are owed to him by the contractor in the event of the contractor being in breach of his obligations under the contract. The bond will usually be for a fixed amount expressed as a percentage of the contract price. These bonds are not expressly provided in the JCT contracts.

Employer's approval of the proposed surety for each bond required should, wherever practicable, be obtained before the contract is executed.

Where a contract requires the contractor to provide a bond, the contract administrator should ensure that the required bond is in place before the contract is entered into.

2.2   Guarantees

Bank guarantees

Bank guarantees are broadly similar to performance bonds, and require all the same safeguards with regards to irrevocability and contractual amendments.

Parent company guarantees

Where the contracting firm is part of a larger group, it is often the practice to seek a guarantee from the parent company that, in the event of any financial difficulties being suffered by the subsidiary, the parent company will ensure that the obligations of the subsidiary will be met. (Note that there is no requirement in English law for a parent company to underwrite the losses of its subsidiary.) Parent companies are frequently reluctant to give such guarantees. The usual reasons given are the necessity of keeping the financial affairs of the two companies separate, and the possibility that the subsidiary might not remain in the control of the parent.

Where a guarantee is available, the normal requirements of English law for writing and consideration should not be forgotten. The guarantee must be either contained in a deed or in writing, with provision for consideration moving from the employer to the parent company. This will usually be some nominal sum, typically £1 or £10, payable on demand.

If a parent company guarantee is in place, it entitles the beneficiary to take court proceedings to enforce it, notwithstanding an arbitration agreement between the other parties. This may be helpful in a case where the surety has little or no defence to the claim, and the beneficiary can seek summary judgment without waiting for the outcome of the arbitration, which may take years to resolve.

3. Collateral warranties

A collateral warranty is an agreement which exists alongside another contract and is related to that other contract. It is a method of joining together parties who in other circumstances would not have a contractual relationship, but who are nevertheless involved in the same undertaking. A collateral warranty may be contained in a deed or a simple contract.

Collateral warranties are commonly used in circumstances such as where a third party (e.g. sub-contractor) is responsible for elements of a design, as an employer will seek to protect his long-term interests by putting in place a direct contractual link with the sub-contractor.

Similarly, if outside funding is being sought, funders seek to protect their investment through collateral warranties providing direct contractual links with the members of the design team.

Thirdly, if there is an intention to sell on the project, or to let it, immediately upon completion, the purchaser or tenant will want to protect their investment by having the ability to sue the provider in the event of defects becoming apparent.

If a contractual warranty is being sought, the aim is to protect the beneficiary as much as possible should the building be defective. On the other hand, the aim of the party giving the warranty is to expose them to as little liability as possible. Ultimately the warranty should not expose the warrantor to any greater exposure than they had under the original contract. That is, a design sub-contractor would only want to owe the same liability to the purchaser of a building as he did to the original developer, and so on.

An important point to remember with collateral warranties is that they create a contractual relationship which enables parties to sue. They do not guarantee the payment of damages, and they are only as good as either the indemnity insurance carried by the individual, firm or company giving the warranty, or the solvency of the warrantor.

Contractors or consultants are under no automatic obligation to give a collateral warranty to anyone at all. The question of whether collateral warranties are to be demanded is one which should be addressed at the start of a project. At that stage it is possible to ensure that every consultant's terms of appointment, and every building contract, contains a term requiring that warranties be given when the client demands it.

JCT contracts which are designed for use on large projects contain the third party rights provisions concerning purchaser's/tenant's and funder's rights from the contractor as an alternative to relevant collateral warranties. The use of the third party rights provisions is growing as it saves the needless effort and costs of securing collateral warranties.

3.1   Standard collateral warranties

The following collateral warranty documents are produced by JCT to be used across a range of contracts specified below.

Contractor Collateral Warranty for a Funder (CWa/F)

The Contractor Collateral Warranty for a Funder is designed for use where a warranty is to be given by the contractor to a separate funder who has entered into an agreement with the employer to provide finance for the works.

It can be used with the following JCT main contracts:

- Standard Building Contract (SBC/Q, SBC/XQ, SBC/AQ)
- Intermediate Building Contract (IC) and Intermediate Building Contract with contractor's design (ICD)
- Design and Build Contract (DB)
- Prime Cost Building Contract (PCC)

Contractor Collateral Warranty for a Purchaser or Tenant (CWa/P&T)

The Contractor Collateral Warranty for a Purchaser or Tenant is designed for use where a warranty is to be given by the contractor to a purchaser(s) or tenant(s) of the whole or part of the building(s) that comprise the works.

It can be used with the following JCT main contracts:

- Standard Building Contract (SBC/Q, SBC/XQ, SBC/AQ)
- Intermediate Building Contract (IC) and Intermediate Building Contract with contractor's design (ICD)
- Design and Build Contract (DB)
- Prime Cost Building Contract (PCC)

Sub-Contractor Collateral Warranty for a Funder (SCWa/F)

The Sub-Contractor Collateral Warranty for a Funder is designed for use where a warranty is to be given by the sub-contractor to a separate funder who has entered into an agreement with the employer to provide finance for the works.

It can be used with a sub-contract let under the following JCT main contracts:

- Standard Building Contract (SBC/Q, SBC/XQ, SBC/AQ)
- Intermediate Building Contract (IC) and Intermediate Building Contract with contractor's design (ICD)
- Design and Build Contract (DB)
- Prime Cost Building Contract (PCC)

Sub-Contractor Collateral Warranty for a Purchaser or Tenant (SCWa/P&T)

The Sub-Contractor Collateral Warranty for a Purchaser or Tenant is designed for use where a warranty is to be given by the sub-contractor to a purchaser(s) or tenant(s) of the whole or part of the building(s) that comprise the works.

It can be used with a sub-contract let under the following JCT main contracts:

- Standard Building Contract (SBC/Q, SBC/XQ, SBC/AQ)
- Intermediate Building Contract (IC) and Intermediate Building Contract with contractor's design (ICD)
- Design and Build Contract (DB)
- Prime Cost Building Contract (PCC)

Sub-Contractor Collateral Warranty for the Employer (SCWa/E)

The Sub-Contractor Collateral Warranty for the Employer is designed for use where a warranty is to be given by the sub-contractor to the employer.

It can be used with a sub-contract let under the following JCT main contracts:

- Standard Building Contract (SBC/Q, SBC/XQ, SBC/AQ)
- Intermediate Building Contract (IC) and Intermediate Building Contract with contractor's design (ICD)
- Design and Build Contract (DB)
- Prime Cost Building Contract (PCC)

3.2 Collateral warranties under the JCT Management Building Contract

The following collateral warranties complement JCT Management Building Contract documents and are only for use on projects let under that contract.

Management Contractor Collateral Warranty for a Funder (MCWa/F)

The Management Contractor Collateral Warranty for a Funder is to be given by the management contractor to a funder who has entered into an agreement with the employer to provide finance for the project.

Management Contractor Collateral Warranty for a Purchaser or Tenant (MCWa/P&T)

This warranty is to be given by the management contractor to a purchaser(s) or tenant(s) of the whole or part of the building(s) that comprises the project.

Works Contractor Collateral Warranty for a Funder (WCWa/F)

This warranty is to be given by the works contractor to a funder who has entered into an agreement with the employer to provide finance for the project.

Works Contractor Collateral Warranty for a Purchaser or Tenant (WCWa/P&T)

This warranty is to be given by the works contractor to a purchaser(s) or tenant(s) of the whole or part of the building(s) that comprises the project.

3.3 Collateral warranties under the JCT Construction Management Contract

The following documents are designed for use with JCT's Construction Management documents and are only for use on projects let under that contract.

Construction Manager Collateral Warranty for a Funder (CMWa/F)

The Construction Manager Collateral Warranty for a Funder is only to be used with a Construction Management Appointment. It is to be given by the construction manager to a funder who has entered into an agreement with the employer to provide finance for the project.

Construction Manager Collateral Warranty for a Purchaser or Tenant (CMWa/P&T)

This warranty is only to be used with a Construction Management Appointment. It is to be given by the construction manager to a purchaser(s) or tenant(s) of the whole or part of the building(s) that comprises the project.

Trade Contractor Collateral Warranty for a Funder (TCWa/F)

This warranty is only to be used with a Trade Contract, and is given by the trade contractor to a funder who has entered into an agreement with the employer to provide finance for the project.

Trade Contractor Collateral Warranty for a Purchaser or Tenant (TCWa/P&T)

This warranty is only to be used with a Trade Contract. It is to be given by the trade contractor to a purchaser(s) or tenant(s) of the whole or part of the building(s) that comprises the project.

Paper 07

Contract administration: Payment

Contents

Aim

Learning outcomes

1. **Introduction**

2. **Parties involved**

3. **Purpose of Interim Payments, Interim Certificates and Payment Notices**

4. **Contractor's entitlement**

5. **Methods of payment**
   5.1 Generally
   5.2 JCT payment provisions and the Housing Grants, Construction and Regeneration Act 1996 as amended by the Local Democracy, Economic Development and Construction Act 2009

6. **Gross Valuations for Interim Certificates and Interim Payment**
   6.1 Measured work – 'work properly executed'
   6.2 Preliminaries
   6.3 Variations
   6.4 Materials on or off site
   6.5 Fluctuations
   6.6 Premiums, fees and charges, etc.
   6.7 Reasonable costs and expenses for suspension because of non-payment
   6.8 Loss and expense
   6.9 Retention

7. **Final accounts**
   7.1 Adjustments
   7.2 Variations
   7.3 Provisional sums and approximate quantities
   7.4 Fluctuations
   7.5 Loss and expense claims

8. **Claims**
   8.1 The need for claims
   8.2 Claims not the answer

Aim

This paper aims to explain how and why payment is made on construction contracts. It covers not only payment for work done but also payments for loss and expense.

Learning outcomes

After studying this paper, you should be able to:

- Explain in detail the procedure for payment using a JCT standard form of building contract with reference to the Standard Building Contract 2011 (SBC) and Design and Build Contract 2011 (DB).
- Understand the basic payment provisions contained in UK legislation regarding payment for construction works.
- Understand how interim and final payments are ascertained and why.
- Understand the factors to be considered prior to compiling a loss and expense claim.
- Understand the significance of the final certificate.
- Understand the importance of monitoring payments and making regular financial reports.

1. Introduction

The most recent legislation in the UK to affect construction payment is the Local Democracy, Economic Development and Construction Act 2009 which amends the Housing Grants, Construction and Regeneration Act 1996 (the Construction Act). Part 8 of the 2009 Act applies to construction contracts in England and Wales that are executed on or after 1 October 2011. The operative date for Scotland was 1 November 2011. The primary legislation is supported by secondary legislation, which for England and Wales is The Scheme for Construction Contracts (England and Wales) Regulations 1998 (Amendment) (England) Regulations 2011 No. 2333. Wales and Scotland have their own Schemes.

The Construction Act requires all construction contracts to include payment provisions that provide for:

- Payment by instalments (periodic or stage payments) for construction contracts of 45 days or more duration.
- An adequate mechanism for determining what amounts are payable and when they are payable.
- A payment notice which can be either led by the payer or led by the payee.
- Such notices to be given within 5 days of the due dates and to state the sum payable (even if zero) and the basis of its calculation.
- The contractor to have the right to suspend performance of any or all of his obligations under the contract if payment is not made within a specified period and to be able to recover reasonable costs and expenses.
- The legislation prohibits the use of provisions that make payment conditional on the performance of obligations under another contract, or by a decision by any person as to whether obligations under another contract have been performed.

The definition of a construction contract is wide but excludes certain operations. The payment legislation does not apply to a construction contract with a residential occupier.

The Act is accompanied by the relevant Scheme for Construction Contracts, which is deemed to be included in the contract if the basic contract either fails to include the necessary provisions or does not otherwise comply with the Act's requirements.

JCT standard forms of contract incorporate provisions that comply with all the legislative requirements and in addition satisfy the Fair Payment Charter. JCT contracts spell out the payment provisions in detail which go beyond that required by legislation so as to assist the contracting parties. Consequently, parties working under such a form need not concern themselves with the wording of the Act or indeed the Scheme. The interpretation of what the provisions of the legislation means in practice is contained within the text of the JCT contract.

JCT has also produced a Public Sector Supplement (see the *Public Sector Supplement* at www.jctltd.co.uk/public-sector.aspx) which, amongst other things, provides for minor modifications to the payment periods so as to precisely follow the Office of Government Commerce's (now Cabinet Office Efficiency and Reform Group) interpretation of fair payment, as set out in its Guide to Best Fair Payment Practice. That Supplement was produced specifically for local authorities and similar organisations funded by central government so as to assist them where there is a requirement to follow strictly the time periods that are set out in the OGC Guide.

The concept of interim payments for construction contracts is rooted in history. In some areas, however, the Construction Act provisions go much further – such as allowing the contractor to suspend contractual performance in the event of non-payment and to recover costs and expenses.

Modern construction projects require a lot of capital. Industry raises capital in various (sometimes expensive) ways and needs certain reserves of working capital to meet its current liabilities. Most companies try to keep close control over their cash flow. If interim payments were not available, the cost of providing the greater amount of capital that would be needed would (or rather should) be priced into the tender sum.

It has often been cheaper for the employer (client) to raise capital on the asset to be constructed and pay the contractor for the value completed (less any retention) as work progresses, than for the contractor to raise and expend all the capital necessary to complete the works before the employer is due to pay anything.

Traditionally valuations have been prepared by reference to the priced contract documentation (e.g. bills of quantities, specification or contract sum analysis), and have been based upon payment of some proportion of the contract sum. The amount due has been calculated either by measurement and valuation at fixed intervals, typically monthly, or alternatively by reference to a list of pre-agreed payments which become due as the contractor reaches predefined milestones in the project programme (i.e. stage payments). Some contractual arrangements, e.g. JCT - Constructing Excellence Contract and JCT Prime Cost Building Contract, provide for the contractor to be paid on the basis of his actual costs, usually on an 'open book' basis. The ease with which building work valuations are made, in order to establish the total value of work properly executed, is dependent upon the nature and detail of the priced document and the extent of variations that are issued. Valuations for contracts using approximate quantities or those based on actual costs can be more complex. Bills of approximate quantities are not to be taken as the actual quantities of works to be executed by the contractor. Consequently all such work must be measured accurately as it progresses so that correct interim payments can be made. By contrast, although the valuation of actual costs is little more than totalling the project costs, the complexity comes about because of determining what costs need to be excluded.

Reasonable accuracy in interim valuation is essential from both the employer's and the contractor's viewpoints because:

- Over-valuation may result in an employer losing the amount of the over valuation, should the contractor become insolvent.
- Under-valuation may put a strain on a contractor's capital reserves and prevent him from proceeding efficiently, leading to a reduction in his margin or even possibly insolvency.

The primary purpose of interim payments is to maintain the contractor's cash flow at a level which is reasonable for the contractor and beneficial to the employer.

2. Parties involved

The Employer

In terms of payment, the employer's obligation is to pay the contractor the Contract Sum or such other sum as shall become payable under the contract at the times and in the manner specified in the conditions. The Contract Sum or adjusted Contract Sum is subject only to the employer's rights of set-off. Any deduction to the notified sum must be detailed in a notice of the payer's intention to pay less than such sum. Note that in addition to the Contract Sum the employer is required to pay any Value Added Tax that is properly chargeable.

If the employer fails in his duty to pay, then the contractor, in addition to being able to suspend all or any of the works having given 7 days' notice, can also give notice of default under the termination provisions. (See Paper 10 *Contract administration: Termination and insolvency* for further detail.)

The Contractor

Under the JCT Standard Building Contract 2011 (SBC) the payment process is 'payer led' Consequently the contractor has no obligation to help in preparing interim valuations or certificates, although in practice the contractor's surveyor will generally work in conjunction with the employer's quantity surveyor who is responsible for preparing the interim valuation. This has the advantage of allowing any problems to be resolved early on. However, this does not relieve the quantity surveyor of his primary responsibility, as he is the person named in the contract to carry out the task of interim valuations.

Despite there being no obligation upon the contractor to prepare interim valuations, the contract does permit him to prepare an application for payment (Interim Application) for submission to the employer's quantity surveyor. Where the contractor does so, the application will, in the event that the contract administrator fails to issue a Certificate, become a Payment Notice.

Under the JCT Design and Build Contract 2011 (DB) there are two payment options. Alternative A, which provides for payment at completion of each stage specified in the Contract Particulars, and Alternative B, which provides for payment on the specified monthly dates.

Although Alternative B is like the position under SBC, the DB payment process is, by contrast, commenced by the contractor as he is under an obligation to make an Interim Application for payment. However, even with this application the employer is still required to issue a payment notice not later than 5 days after the due date.

Under Alternative A, the due date is the later of the date of completion of the stage and the date of receipt of the contractor's application. Under Alternative B, the due date is the later of the specified date and the date of receipt of the contractor's application. If the employer fails to issue a Payment Notice then the sum stated as due in the contractor's application becomes the amount of the interim payment. If deductions are to be made, the employer must issue a Pay Less Notice.

The Contract Administrator

Under SBC, interim payments by the employer shall be on the monthly dates (due dates) specified in the Contract Particulars and the contract administrator must issue Interim Certificates no later than 5 days after each of those dates. Where no date is stated in the Contract Particulars, the first due date is one month after the Date of Possession and the same monthly date thereafter. Before certifying the amount for payment, the contract administrator should ensure there is no defective work: he should deduct from the quantity surveyor's valuation the value of any work he determines is improperly executed, or of any materials that have been prematurely brought on to the site or are not adequately protected.

The Quantity Surveyor

Under SBC, the quantity surveyor is responsible for preparing interim valuations and deciding the amount to be recommended to the contract administrator prior to issue of the Interim Certificate.

Under DB, as we saw earlier, the contractor is required to make an Interim Application based on a Gross Valuation to the employer who is then required to issue a Payment Notice. The employer will often engage a quantity surveyor to check the contractor's valuation and advise the employer accordingly prior to the employer issuing the Payment Notice which has to be issued within the 5 day period.

3. Purpose of Interim Payments, Interim Certificates and Payment Notices

The main purpose of paying the contractor by instalments is to help the contractor's cash flow and to reduce the cost of finance. Interim certificates and payment notices are a means of notifying the parties of the amount payable for the work that has been carried out, together with any other items that are to be included under the contract.

However, the issue of an Interim Certificate does not confirm acceptance of the quality of the workmanship or materials and shall not of itself be conclusive that they are in accordance with the contract. It is the intention that such work, etc. that is included in the Interim Certificate does comply, and the contract makes it clear that any work containing defects is not accepted. Consequently, sums included in one certificate may be omitted in a later one.

Because cash flow is so important not only for contractors but also for the supply chain, other means have been sought for making interim payments. One such means is the Project Bank Account which is intended to shorten the periods that the supply chain has to wait to be paid for 'certified' work. See JCT's Project Bank Account Documentation 2011 for the detailed provisions (www.jctltd.co.uk/product/project-bank-account).

Paper 07   Contract administration: Payment

4. Contractor's entitlement

For interim payments, the contractor is entitled to be paid the full value of all work properly completed at the date of the valuation, including the value of any sub-contractor's work, variations and the other items listed under the provisions of the Gross Valuation (dealt with below), including any sums calculated under the fluctuation rules. The valuation should be applied to work, etc. up to and including a date not more than 7 days before the due date of an interim payment.

The employer may however, where the contract provides, retain a proportion (the Retention), as stated in the Contract Particulars, of the money due. This is a form of security against future failure of the contractor to properly make good any defects appearing before the end of the contract Rectification Period. Even where Retention applies, not all of the sums which are included in the valuation will be subject to such Retention. Under SBC, for example, the items subject to Retention are:

- Value of work, including variations, sub-contractor's work, Confirmed Acceptance of an Acceleration Quotation and formula fluctuations adjustments, where applicable.
- Unfixed materials for the project that have been delivered to and placed on or adjacent to the works, provided that they are delivered at an appropriate time and are properly stored and protected.
- Materials off site, provided that they are itemised in a list (Listed Items) attached to the bills of quantities or specification/work schedule, as the case may be, and comply with the additional requirements of clause 4.17 (SBC).

Items not subject to Retention are:

- Premiums, fees and charges (2.6.2)
- Royalties (2.21, 2.23)
- Inspections and tests (3.17)
- Suspension costs and expenses (4.14.2)
- Insurances (6.5.3, 6.10.2 or 6.10.3)
- Loss and expense payments (4.23)
- Restoration, replacement or repair in respect of insurance claims (B.3.5, C.4.5.2 of Schedule 3 or 6.11.5.2)
- Conventional fluctuations (Fluctuations Options A or B)

The amount payable by the employer is the gross value, as calculated above (subject to any agreement between the Parties as to stage payments) less Retention, the total amount stated as due in previous certificates, any sums paid in respect of an Interim Payment Notice given after the issue of the latest Interim Certificate and the cumulative total of amounts of any advance payment due for reimbursement.

5. Methods of payment

5.1 Generally

There are several methods of paying a building contractor for the work he carries out for a client. The arrangements will be clearly laid down in the form of contract used. The most common methods are:

- **After completion**
  Payment is made after the total contract works have been completed. This can only arise where the duration of the works is agreed to be less than 45 days. Consequently, this normally would only apply to very small scale works.

- **Stage payments**
  Payments are made at certain stages, e.g. work up to damp course; work from damp course to roofing. Stage payments are generally more appropriate to housing contracts or repetitive type work, where each stage can be readily defined and valued. Figure 07- 1 shows the breakdown of the various stages and valuation of a house.

FIGURE 07-1 Breakdown of stage payments for typical house

Stages	*£*
Work up to damp-proof course	
External and internal walls, windows, doors, roof	
Internal finishings, plumbing, electrics	
External works	
Total	

- **Periodic payments**
  Payments are made to the contractor as the work proceeds, generally on a monthly basis. However, the interval between payments is not defined by legislation and is at the discretion of the parties to the contract but clearly if this is too long it will defeat the main purpose of periodic payments and the intentions of the Fair Payment Charter.

5.2 JCT payment provisions and the Housing Grants, Construction and Regeneration Act 1996 as amended by the Local Democracy, Economic Development and Construction Act 2009

All JCT standard forms of building contract incorporate payment provisions that comply with the Construction Act, which are standard insofar as they can be. The precise

arrangements are dependent on the contract. For instance, under DB, there is no named contract administrator and the payment process is triggered by the contractor.

The following is the position under SBC:

Not later than 5 days after each due date for interim payment, the contract administrator shall issue an Interim Certificate, stating the sum he considers due for payment, what it is for, and how it has been calculated.

The provisions state that the final date for payment of an interim payment shall be 14 days from its due date. This means that the employer has 14 days (9 days from the latest date for issue of the Interim Certificate), including weekends but not public holidays, after the due date to pay the contractor. Where an Interim Certificate is not issued, the contractor's Interim Application becomes an Interim Payment Notice. If he has not made an application, the contractor may give an Interim Payment Notice after 5 days from the due date and the final date for payment is postponed by the number of days after expiry of the 5 day period that the Interim Payment Notice is given.

If the employer intends to pay less than the amount due under an Interim Certificate or Interim Payment Notice, he must not later than 5 days before the final date for payment, notify the contractor, in a Pay Less Notice, the sum he considers is due and the basis of its calculation. The time scale for issuing the Pay Less Notice is short and the employer will need to act promptly if he believes he should pay less than the amount stated in the certificate or payment notice.

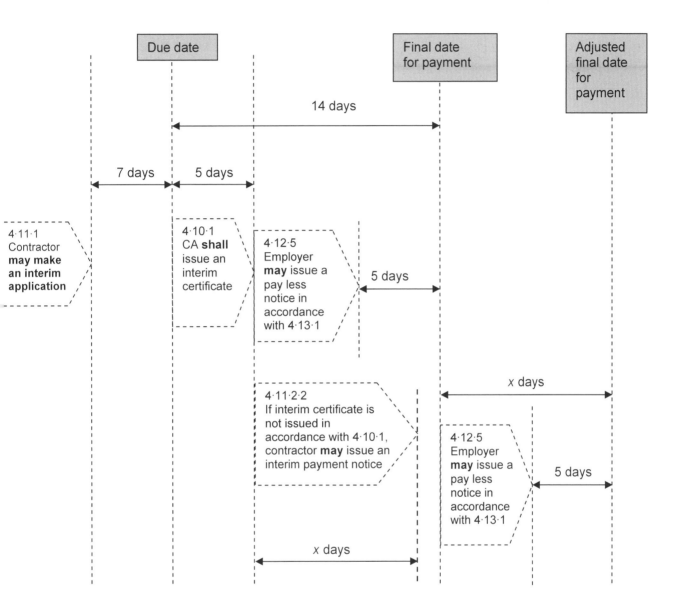
FIGURE 07-2 Interim payment procedure under SBC
(Credit: *Guide to SBC11* by Sarah Lupton, RIBA Publishing)

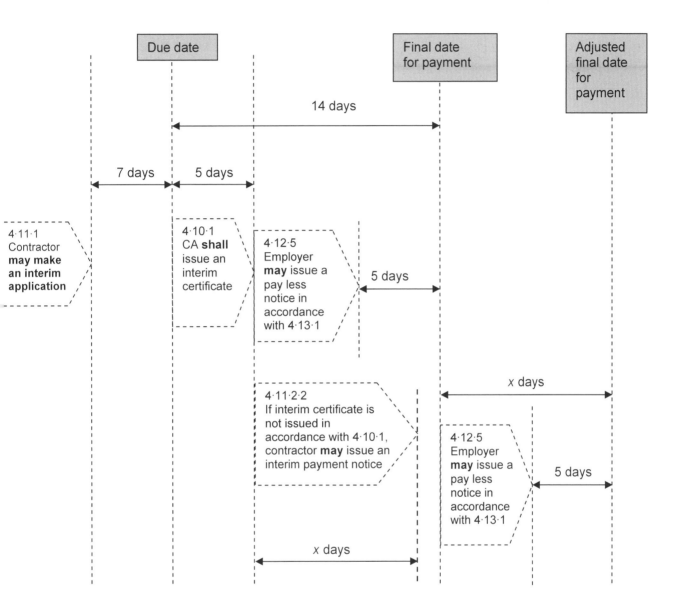

If there is no Pay Less Notice within the stated time periods, the employer must pay the amount of the Interim Certificate or Interim Payment Notice by the final date for payment. Failure to do so would be a breach of contract and the contractor can start claiming interest on any outstanding amount. Interest is payable at 5% above the official dealing rate of the Bank of England current at the date the payment becomes overdue. See also the right of suspension and or termination, as referred to above and below, where there is failure to pay. To suspend the works, the contractor notifies the employer, with a copy to the contract administrator, of his intention to suspend the performance of his obligations due to non-payment. If the default continues for 7 days after giving notice, the contractor may suspend performance of all or any of his obligations until payment is made in full.

In practice (and as an alternative), consideration should be given to starting adjudication proceedings, as suspension causes considerable disruption to work. The position under DB follows the same approach, except that there is no Interim Certificate: the contractor is required to make an Interim Application and the employer issues a Payment Notice.

6. Gross Valuations for Interim Certificates and Interim Payment

The Gross Valuation under SBC and Alternative B (Periodic payments) of DB should include the following items:

- Measured work (contained in the contract documents), including any adjustment by Confirmed Acceptance of an Acceleration Quotation
- Preliminaries
- Value of variations
- Materials on site
- Off-site materials (Listed items)
- Fluctuations in costs of labour, and/or taxes
- Premiums, fees and charges, royalties, inspections and tests, insurances
- Reasonable costs and expenses for suspension because of non-payment (4.14.2)
- Loss and expense
- Restoration, replacement, etc. in respect of insurance claims (B.3.5, C.4.5.2 of Schedule 3 or 6.11.5.2)

And deduct any of the following:

- Setting out (2.10)
- Defects (2.38)
- Non-compliance with instructions (3.11)
- Work not in accordance with the contract (3.18.2)
- Conventional fluctuations – amounts allowable by contractor (Options A or B)

Alternative A under DB deals with the Gross Valuation differently because it provides for the value of stages as set out in the Contract Particulars.

The following notes describe the method of arriving at the value of the main items.

6.1   Measured work – 'work properly executed'

Where there is a priced bill of quantities, the process simply consists of going through the bill item by item and extracting the value of completed and partly completed items. Unless the items are particularly expensive, the proportions of those which are incomplete generally may be assessed by visual inspection rather than precise measurement.

Note that the quantity surveyor, in valuing the works, includes all work properly executed. Although they have no authority to decide whether or not work has been 'properly executed' he should note in his valuation any items included which he believes may be defective. The decision as to what is not properly executed rests with the contract administrator, who has the opportunity to revise the valuation to take account of such work before issuing the Interim Certificate.

Under DB the valuation is carried out by the contractor as part of his Interim Application. The contractor should only include work 'properly executed' but if the application includes work that is not then the onus is on the employer to exclude it when issuing his Payment Notice or Pay Less Notice.

6.2   Preliminaries

The preliminaries section of the contract documents contains important financial matters relating to the contract as a whole, not necessarily to any specific item or section – e.g. water for works, lighting and power for the project, temporary buildings, site supervision and insurances.

Preliminary items can be grouped into different categories:

- **Initial and final costs**
  Initial costs are generally lump sums related to site establishment, expended early in the contract period or in the early stages of an item. For example, the supply of a temporary road will be at the beginning of the contract but the transport and erection of scaffolding may not be until some months into the contract. Both, however, are lump sum initial costs and should be paid for when the cost is incurred.

  Final costs are related to site clearance at the end of the project. They are lump sums expended at the end of the contract or towards the end of an item's use.

- **Cost-related items**
  An example of a cost-related item is water for the works. The cost will depend on the work content and is usually quoted as a percentage of the contract value.

- **Time-related items**
  Time-related items include items such as site supervision, hire of site facilities, etc., expended over the contract period and not necessarily related to the contract value.

- **Combination of types**
  Many preliminaries items include a mixture of those types of cost. Figure 07-3 shows an example of the work involved in supplying and operating a tower crane.

FIGURE 07-3 What's in a price?

£

Allow for supplying and operating
a track-mounted crane

This may cover:

Base:	put down labour and material:			I
	take up and remove:			F
Track:	lay:	Crane:	erect:	I
	hire:		hire:	T
	remove:		dismantle:	F
Transport:	to site:			I
	from site:			F
Fuel cost:	electricity:			T
Operator:				T
Temporary electric supply:	bring in:			I
	remove:			F

I = Initial cost
F = Final cost
T = Time-related cost

Valuation of the preliminaries section may be carried out using a detailed breakdown as shown above but other ways are used, such as:

- **Proportion per month**. Obtained by dividing the total preliminaries amount by the number of months in the contract period, giving a constant amount for inclusion in each valuation. However, this does not take into account that the work may be behind programme, which could result in the total preliminaries being paid well before completion and conversely where the contractor is in advance of the programme.

- **Percentage of value**. Preliminaries are expressed as a percentage of the contract sum to be added to the monthly value of the contractor's measured work.

Neither of these approaches takes account of when the preliminaries are actually expended and consequently neither is as accurate as using a detailed breakdown.

6.3 Variations

Most projects have variations and as we have seen these need to be valued in Interim Certificates. Ideally, the amount of a variation, whether by a formal quotation or otherwise, should be sought and agreed prior to issuing an instruction to vary the works. This can avoid a disagreement arising later but unfortunately it is not always possible to do so because there is insufficient time before an instruction has to be issued. Where pre-agreement is not possible, attention must be given to measuring and valuing these instructions before each valuation so that it can be included in the interim payment. If subsequent agreement between the employer and contractor cannot be reached, the variation is valued in accordance with the Valuation Rules set out in the contract.

6.4 Materials on or off site

The value of materials and goods delivered to the site are to be included in the Gross Valuation. However, under Alternative A of DB, there is no express provision covering materials on site, and they would only be paid for if their value had been included in the stated stage payment.

The task of ascertaining the quantities of materials on site is made easier if the site agent and clerk of works produce an agreed list for checking. Again, attention generally will be concentrated on the more expensive items.

In order to be included in the Gross Valuation, materials on site must be:

- In accordance with the specification
- Intended for use in the works
- Delivered at an appropriate time (i.e. not unreasonably early)
- Properly stored and protected against damage, theft, deterioration, etc.

The materials may be valued by reference to a basic price list, or at current market prices, or from invoices supplied by the contractor. A difficulty might arise where a bill item has been under-priced and the invoice price of the material is higher than the bill rate for both labour and materials (something that should have been identified at tender evaluation stage). In such cases, a price for the material must be agreed which is consistent with the bill rate.

Off-site materials should also be included in the Gross Valuation but only insofar as:

- They are listed in a schedule attached to the contract documents
- The property in the materials is vested in the contractor
- They are insured and are clearly marked as required by the contract

6.5 Fluctuations

JCT contracts provide three Fluctuations Options, namely 'contribution, levy and tax fluctuations' only (Option A), 'labour and materials cost and tax fluctuations' (Option B) and 'formula adjustment' (Option C). In the past, fluctuations provisions have been used regularly but in recent times their use has reduced substantially. Because of their limited use and the high level of detail necessary to understand their operation it is not proposed to deal with them here. For further information on dealing with fluctuations please refer to Chapter 5 of *Presentation and Settlement of Contractors' Claims* by G. Trickey and M. Hackett (Spon Press 2000). Although this book deals with the fluctuations provisions of an earlier edition of the JCT Standard Form of Contract, the principles remain valid.

6.6   Premiums, fees and charges, etc.

Where they apply, the cost of sundry items, such as premiums, fees and charges, royalties, inspections and tests, and insurances, are determined and included in the valuation. The various amounts generally can be established by reference to invoices and premium receipts.

6.7   Reasonable costs and expenses for suspension because of non-payment

In respect of suspension costs and expenses the evaluation will be complex and more like the approach to loss and expense.

6.8   Loss and expense

Where the regular progress of the works is affected by any of the matters (Relevant Matters) provided for in the contract, the contractor should make an application to the contract administrator (employer under DB). Any loss and expense arising from disturbance of the regular progress of the works, unless the contract states there shall be no addition to the contract sum for a particular item, is to be assessed by the contract administrator or (if he so instructs) the quantity surveyor, and included in the Gross Valuation. Loss and expense may also arise following a deferment of possession of site, where deferment is provided for under clause 2.5.

6.9   Retention

The total value of the work and materials is subject to Retention of 3% unless a different rate is stated. The objective of retention is to provide an incentive for the contractor to complete his obligations quickly, and to give the employer some financial security if the contractor defaults. The use of retention has been widely criticised because it is suggested that it does not satisfy those objectives. For those averse to retention it is possible to insert a nil percentage. Alternatively the contractor may be required to take out a bond for the due completion of the work. Bond-holders are sometimes banks but more usually insurance companies specialising in this work.

The application of the Retention Percentage depends on whether work has reached practical completion (full retention percentage); thereafter it is half of the percentage rate until the works have been made good.

Retention monies are held in trust and at the request of the contractor (except where the employer is a local authority) may ask for the money to be put into a separate bank account.

Because of the status of retention monies there are strict rules governing how they are dealt with.

7. Final accounts

It is, of course, essential at the end of the contract to have a proper settlement of the final financial position between the employer and the main contractor, and this settlement document is usually termed the 'final account'. Under contracts where a quantity surveyor is employed, the preparation of the final account document will be his responsibility. In other cases, the account will usually be prepared by the contractor for checking and approval by the contract administrator/employer. Under SBC the contractor has 6 months from the issue of the Practical Completion Certificate in which to supply the necessary documents to the contract administrator or (if so instructed) the quantity surveyor to enable them to make the appropriate adjustments to the Contract Sum. The quantity surveyor then has up to 3 months (in practice just under three months) from receipt of that information to prepare a statement. The contract administrator within the same 3 month period has to ascertain any loss and expense and send a copy of the quantity surveyor's statement and their own ascertainment of loss and expense to the contractor.

For lump sum contracts such as those let on a bill of quantities, preparation of the final account will be on the basis of additions to and omissions from the original contract sum to take account of any variations which have arisen; whereas for contracts let on approximate quantities, the account will comprise a complete re-measurement of the work 'as built'.

When preparing the final account, the provisions of the contract must be observed strictly. The contract sum must not be adjusted or altered in any way other than in strict accordance with the express provisions of the contract. What follows is a description of a typical final account process for a lump sum project prepared on an 'add and omit' basis.

Before beginning the measurement and valuation, it is necessary to collect and cross-reference all the source documents. In addition to those mentioned earlier for interim valuations, these include:

- Contract administrator's instructions
- Copies of minutes of site meetings
- Daywork sheets
- Wages sheets
- Materials invoices for conventional fluctuations

It is also helpful to establish the final format of the account, which will provide a framework within which to organise the measurements.

The following is a simplified version of a common form of presentation:

FINAL ACCOUNT
Office block

Main summary	Omissions £	Additions £
Contract sum		
Less Contingencies		
Variations on contractor's work		
Adjustment of provisional sums		
Adjustment of provisional quantities		
Dayworks		
Fluctuations (contractor)		
Less Omissions		
Less Amounts stated as due in interim certificates 1 to x		
Balance outstanding		

The full list of items which should be considered under clause 4.3 (SBC) is as follows:

7.1   Adjustments

The Contract Sum is to be adjusted by:

- Amounts agreed in respect of Variations, etc.
- Amounts of Variation Quotation and Acceleration Quotation where there is a Confirmed Acceptance
- Any variation in insurance premium under clause 6.10.2 (Insurance Option A)

Deductions:

- Provisional sums and approximate quantities
- Valuation of Variations – omissions
- Amounts due to the employer in respect of inaccurate setting out (where it is agreed it shall remain), defects not to be made good, non-compliance with instructions, work not in accordance with the contract that is to remain and remedial measures under the fire code
- Fluctuations – amounts allowable to employer
- Any other amount required by the contract to be deducted from the Contract Sum

Additions:

- Amounts payable to the contractor in respect of:
  - fees and charges

- - o patent rights
  - o inspections and tests
  - o insurance of liability of employer
- Valuation of Variations – additions
- Value of work executed in respect of provisional sums and approximate quantities
- Loss and expense payments
- Amounts paid under Insurance Options B or C or in respect of additional premiums because of early use by employer, terrorism insurance premiums and compliance with changes (after the base date) to the fire code
- Fluctuations payable
- Costs and expenses related to the contractor's right of suspension owing to non-payment
- Any other amount which is required by this contract to be added to the Contract Sum

The main elements of the final account are dealt with as follows:

7.2 Variations

Variations may be the subject of contractor's quotations, or may need to be measured and valued according to the contract's Valuation Rules.

SBC provides the contractor an opportunity to be present when the quantity surveyor is measuring the work. Usually the prices to be charged are also discussed at the meeting. However, failing agreement, the quantity surveyor must use their own judgement in applying the Valuation Rules to fix prices. If the contractor is dissatisfied, they have a remedy in adjudication and arbitration.

Before valuing variations, the quantity surveyor should make sure that there is a written instruction for the work, or that the contractual procedures have been followed with regard to oral instructions. The only exceptions are changes which, under the terms of the contract, are to be corrected, such as errors in bills of quantities. These do not require any authorising instruction, although the contractor may be under an obligation to give notice before proceeding with the work. So if changes are necessary in order to comply with any regulation or bye-law, the contractor must give notice of the change to the contract administrator.

Difficulties sometimes arise in respect of the position of the clerk of works who acts as an inspector on behalf of the contract administrator. The role and function of the clerk of works are set out in the contract, and their ability to issue directions to the contractor that has contractual effect is closely circumscribed. Quantity surveyors therefore need to be very careful where contractors contend that additional costs have been incurred as a result of the clerk of works' actions: they need to ensure that any such direction has been confirmed by the contract administrator.

The quantity surveyor should keep a file of variation orders, together with related correspondence, site notes (photographs) and measurements of work that will be hidden when complete. Here it may be helpful to enlist the help of the clerk of works, though measuring the work is not strictly part of his duties. In some cases it is possible to premeasure varied work from drawings; in other cases it is necessary to wait until the work has been completed so that it can be measured physically on site. The frequency of site visits for this purpose depends on the size and complexity of the works and the need to take vital measurements before the work is covered up.

It is important that variations should be measured as soon as possible after execution so that there is an up-to-date picture of the financial state of the contract.

Generally it is advantageous to group related variations, especially where there are variations *on* variations. Each variation order or group of orders should be taken in turn, omitting the work contained in the contract bills* and adding back the measurements for the new work. It is advisable to start the dimensions for each variation or group of variations on a fresh page under a heading giving the order number, date issued, date measured and a brief description for identification. To avoid confusion, some surveyors use red for omissions and black for additions.

*In this section the reference is to contract bills assuming a 'With Quantities' version of SBC, whereas the 'Without Quantities' version refers to contract documents: DB refers to a Contract Sum Analysis.

Where the whole of a bill item is omitted, only the bill reference needs be stated. Otherwise the measurements for the part to be omitted may be obtained from the original taking-off.

The method of valuing variations depends on whether the varied work is of a similar character and executed under similar conditions to the work in the contract bills and does not significantly change the quantity of that work, and whether it is capable of being measured, as illustrated in Figure 07-4.

FIGURE 07-4 Valuation of variations

Measured valuations

Character	Conditions		Quantity		Method
Character	*Conditions*		*Quantity*		*Method*
Similar	Similar		Similar		Measure
				×	Bill rates
Similar	Different	and/or	Different		Measure
				×	Bill rates
				+	Fair allowance
Different	N/A		N/A		Measure
				×	Fair rates

In the case of daywork, the contractor is allowed the 'prime cost' calculated in accordance with the 'definition of prime cost of daywork carried out under a building contract' issued by the RICS and the Construction Confederation, together with percentage additions to each section – i.e. labour, materials and plant – at the rates set out by the contractor in the contract bills. The contractor must submit to the contract administrator vouchers specifying workmen's names, the time spent daily on the work, and the plant and materials used, not later than 7 days after the work was carried out. These vouchers are then verified by the contract administrator.

An alternative method which is sometimes adopted is to ask the tenderer to quote all-inclusive rates for labour instead of a percentage addition to the basic rate. Any all-inclusive rates will be stated in the contract bills.

When checking daywork accounts, consider the following:

- Ensure that the work cannot in fact be measured properly and that there is no overlap with work covered in measured items. The mere submission of vouchers by the contractor is no guarantee that the work will be valued on that basis.
- Check that the operative times claimed tally with the voucher signed by the clerk of works or other, and that the wage rates are those current at the time the work was carried out. The hours worked should be deducted from those on which any fluctuations are calculated.
- Check that the quantities of materials are reasonable in relation to the work carried out. Trade discounts should be deducted and the price adjusted, if necessary, to reflect the permitted cash discount. Where materials have been supplied from the contractor's stock, the price should be the market price at the date of supply.
- Check that the plant used was solely for the daywork during the period claimed and that the hire charges are as agreed.

7.3   Provisional sums and approximate quantities

These sums are included for work, whether or not identified as being defined or undefined, that cannot be entirely foreseen at the time of tendering. The contract administrator is required to issue instructions where the expenditure of provisional sums is required. Where the work is carried out by the contractor, it is valued in accordance with the Valuation Rules unless a quotation for such work has been agreed or it is otherwise agreed by the employer and contractor.

Sometimes 'approximate quantities' are given for sections of the work or individual items where only the quantity is in doubt, and it is desired to obtain competitive rates for valuing the work on re-measurement. Approximate quantities differ from provisional sums in that there is a rate determined for each item. However, where the quantity is not a reasonably accurate forecast of the actual quantity, the rate will only form the basis of a valuation and should also include a fair allowance.

7.4   Fluctuations

The methods of determining the amount of fluctuations have been referred to earlier under 6.5 (*Fluctuations*). Where fluctuations do apply, it is proper (the contract requires) that one attends to these adjustments during the progress of the contract and not to leave them until

completion. This ensures that interim payments reflect the correct amount and also assists with the financial reporting process.

7.5 Loss and expense claims

The assessment of loss and expense claims is dealt with in the following section.

8. Claims

8.1 The need for claims

Claims always arouse a great deal of interest, but can seem shrouded in an aura of mystery. However, it should be noted that in JCT contracts the word 'claim' does not appear – it is in essence an adjustment to the Contract Sum. In specified circumstances, the contractor is entitled to reimbursement of proven loss and expense but first they must give notice of such loss and expense. In most cases the loss is ascertained by the contract administrator, or the quantity surveyor (SBC). The contractor's obligation is limited to providing the information requested that is necessary to allow the assessment to be made. In order to do this it is important that the contractor keeps proper detailed records.

An ideal contract would be one where all the information was complete in every detail before the start, no variations were issued, the project was completed on time, and the contractor made his anticipated profit. This situation seldom, if ever, arises and where changes are made to the contract, or the conditions under which the project is carried out, then the contractor is likely to try to make good his financial position by means of a claim. In practice it is often found that the wrong contract is used for the level of design that has been reached at tender stage; for example, the Standard Building Contract With Quantities instead of the Standard Building Contract With Approximate Quantities, thus aggravating the situation regarding the emergence of claims and the view some people have of them.

'Claim' is defined as:

- 'The demand of a right or supposed right' *(New British Dictionary)*.
- 'Demand for something due, an assertion of a right to something' *(Oxford English Dictionary)*.

The main point is the word 'right': it is an entitlement. However, it must not be imaginary. For claims to be successful they must be based on fact and have their origins in the contract.

It follows, therefore, that the conditions of contract and contract documents used must be looked at when judging whether a claim is permissible. Any ambiguity or conflict in the documents will make the claim more difficult to decide.

The word 'claim', therefore, should be used to denote a request by a contractor for some additional payment arising from carrying out new work, dealing with maintenance work, or providing a service under the contract, whether the value of the work is large or small. In fact, any work carried out by means of a contract may give rise to claims for reimbursement of loss and expense.

8.2 Claims not the answer

Bankruptcies or liquidations of businesses, particularly in the construction industry, are rarely caused solely by failures in the standard of work. They are more likely to be due to poor management, deficiencies in the financial control systems, lack of funding and inappropriate pricing.

Clearly claims are not the answer to all financial worries and are not meant to reimburse the contractor for bad management or items for which the contractor has assumed the contractual risk. They do not cover for:

- Wrong decisions at tender:
    - incorrect tender value
    - uneconomic schedule rates
    - underestimating difficulties of the project
    - incorrect assessment of contract period.
- Poor management:
    - poor control
    - poor utilisation of plant.
- Poor financial control in:
    - picking up variations
    - recording dayworks
    - submitting payment and fluctuation requests.

It is not the employer's responsibility to reimburse a contractor for his own deficiencies. Nor does it follow that if a contractor has made a loss on a project he must therefore have a claim.

8.3 Origin of a claim

Claims occur for a variety of reasons, the main ones being:

- Deferment of possession
- Late issue of instructions
- Failure of the employer
- Divergence between contract documents
- Variations*
- Expenditure of an undefined provisional sum
- Postponement of work

* Note, however, that the contractual valuation rules may mean that payment for variations is not necessarily related directly to the contractor's costs. SBC, for example, relates the valuation of variations to decisions made by the contractor at tender stage, not to the actual costs involved. Loss and expense is only relevant where the regular progress of the work has been materially affected.

8.4   Admissible items under a claim

Sometimes referred to as the 'heads of claim', these are the items which will be considered for payment:

- Cost of running the site during an extension period for Relevant Matters
- Disruption, where there is no delay to the work but additional cost, e.g. uneconomic working of labour or plant
- Head office overheads
- Loss of profit
- Fluctuations
- Finance charges

8.5   Assessing the value

Work will not necessarily go according to plan but it is possible to ease the problem of assessing the value of some areas of claims by anticipating them in the tender documentation. For example, schedules of prices for plant and labour can be included that will facilitate assessment and, if necessary, form the basis of calculating additional work items. In the absence of such prices, it will be necessary to look at each submission in detail.

For those interested in detailed information on claims, please refer to the book entitled *Presentation and Settlement of Contractors' Claims* by G. Trickey and M. Hackett (Spon Press 2000).

9. Final Certificate and Final Payment

The last part of the payment process, the final payment is set out in the Final Certificate (SBC) and Final Statement (DB).

Under SBC, the contract administrator has a 2 month period from the latest of one of three dates in which to issue the Final Certificate. Those dates relate to end of the Rectification Period, Certificate of Making Good or the date of the contract administrator's statement and ascertainment (final account). Clearly, the final account must be complete before the Final Certificate can be issued.

The Final Certificate is required to state:

- The Contract Sum as adjusted under the contract, and
- The total sum due in Interim Certificates, any advance payments and any sums in an Interim Payment Notice given after the issue of the latest Interim Certificate.

The difference between the two sums should be shown as the balance due (final payment) to the contractor or employer as the case may be. The due date for the final payment is the date of issue of the Final Certificate unless it is not issued within the prescribed 2 month period.

Where it is not issued within such period the due date is, subject to clause 4.15.6, the last day of that period. The amount due must then be paid within 28 days from that date unless some other amount is stated to be due in a Pay Less Notice which can be given not later than 5 days before the final date for payment, i.e. 23 days from the due date. Where the Final Certificate is not issued in accordance with the provisions of the contract, clause 4.15.6 provides that the contractor may then issue a Final Payment Notice.

The issue of the Final Certificate is important for a number of reasons but in terms of payment it becomes conclusive evidence (unless adjudication, arbitration or other proceedings have been commenced prior to its issue) that all the necessary adjustments have been made to the Contract Sum except for accidental inclusions and exclusions or errors in computation.

The position under DB is different because there is a Final Statement, rather than a final certificate, which is prepared by the contractor. The statement sets out the adjusted Contract Sum and the amounts paid. The difference between these sums is then treated as described above. The Final Statement should be submitted within 3 months of practical completion. If the contractor does not do so, the employer may give a notice to the effect that if they do not do so within a further 2 months, the employer will issue the statement.

10. Financial reports

The importance of cost control services, both pre- and post-contract, has increased greatly in recent years, owing partly to financial conditions and partly to clients' demands to start projects quickly without full preparation. It is generally accepted that, where time permits, a fully pre-planned contract with accurate documentation (which may be bills of quantities) allows much greater control over expenditure than can otherwise be obtained. On the other hand, there is little point in trying to produce an accurate bill of quantities if the design is not complete at the time of determining the price. In such cases an approximate bill of quantities is more appropriate and more truly reflects the position.

The essence of cost control is the frequent and regular reporting by the quantity surveyor of the financial state of the contract to the employer. Although the quantity surveyor has no direct control over the ordering of variations, he can predict their cost consequences and so make the employer aware of the financial commitment before the work is put in hand. This demands a close working relationship between the contract administrator and the quantity surveyor and is really a continuation of the initial cost planning process.

The quantity surveyor should arrange for the contract administrator and the other consultants to inform him about proposed instructions and other matters that affect the contract financially as soon as they become known – preferably before the instructions are issued to the contractor. The quantity surveyor should also keep in touch with the contractor to receive early warning of any changes that he may see as necessary.

Many disputes that arise on building contracts could be avoided by better communication and regular, formalised reporting on the physical and financial state of the work. The quantity surveyor's contribution to this is the preparation of financial statements. These form a running total of the estimated final cost, taking into account predicted variations, fluctuations and possible claims for loss and expense, so that the employer and the contract administrator can have an up-to-date picture of the financial state of the contract.

It is recommended that financial statements (example shown in Figure 07-5) are sent to the contract administrator for comment before forwarding to the client. A covering letter can explain any items that are in doubt, such as the amount of possible future claims from the contractor.

FIGURE 07-5 Example financial statement

Financial statement

No...as...

For ....

Contract period...weeks. Extension...................................weeks.

Date for completion ....

AUTHORISED COMMITMENT
1   Contract sum
2   Client's revised requirements
3   Fluctuations

VARIATIONS AND ADJUSTMENTS
4   Omission of provisional sums for contingencies and daywork
5   Adjustment of approximate quantities and provisional sums
6   Other Contract Administrator's instructions
7   Instructions confirmed by contractor but for which Contract Administrator's instructions have not been issued
8   Anticipated variations in cost for which no formal instructions have been issued
9   Amount of 'direct loss and/or expense' resulting from disturbance to the regular progress of the works
     ESTIMATED FINAL COST   £
     Net under/overspend   £

LIQUIDATED DAMAGES

Following the issue by the Contract Administrator of his certificate under clause .... of

the Conditions of Contract, the Employer may elect to claim liquidated damages amounting

to £......................... unless further extensions of time are granted, assuming completion by

....

CLAIMS

Claims lodged but not included above £ ....

Paper 08

Contract administration: Control of the works

Contents

Aim

This paper aims to explain how the JCT contract clauses can influence the way the quality of the work is controlled.

Learning outcomes

After studying this paper you should be able to:

- Explain and comment on the contract provisions for controlling the works and quality
- Discuss the roles and responsibilities of those involved in quality control
- Understand what action can be taken regarding defective work

1. Introduction

This paper is primarily in relation to traditional JCT contracts such as the Standard Building Contract and explains how traditional JCT contracts make provision for controlling the quality of the works on a project, and the roles of the employer, contractor and contract administrator under the contract to ensure that the obligations regarding quality are maintained. In addition, this paper will also discuss work that does not meet the required standards, known as defects, and the process under the contract for dealing with them.

Controlling the quality of the works is established before construction work begins and, in the case where defects are discovered after construction is complete, can continue beyond the contract phase. Generally, the quality to which the works should be carried out and completed is outlined in the contract documents.

Many contract documents refer to published standards with regard to the quality required, e.g. British Standards, ISO. However, other terms regarding quality of work are also implied in the contract. The courts now regard contractors as experts in construction, who are required to bring any design defects they believe exist to the contract administrator's notice. This does not require knowledge of a specific error but a belief that there may be a problem or a likelihood of subsequent failure.

Having established in the contract documents the required standards, the contract conditions should provide for inspection of the works to establish whether those standards are met, and state procedures for correcting defects.

Regular inspection of the works is normal. Most standard forms of contract prescribe an inspection regime but, if not, it must be decided who will do the inspection, and when, as soon as a contract is awarded. Some contractors, where they do not design, consider quality inspection and control to be entirely the contract administrator's responsibility. However, Latham and Egan both stress that achieving satisfactory quality should be a priority for all involved – hence the present cultural changes to put in place a 'right first time' attitude.

The client may decide what inspections they require, and the contractor may wish to make further inspections of sub-contractors' work. For traditional and management contracts these may be weekly, as the main contractor asks for clarification of details and checks are made prior to interim valuations. For a design and build project, however, there is reduced need for regular communication between the client's representative and the main contractor, and specific visits to site may be arranged to inspect the works.

2. Statutory obligations

Statutory obligations arise through legislation. Contractors must, of course, comply with their statutory responsibilities, and breach of them may give rise to either a criminal or a civil liability. A criminal liability would arise if, for example, the work carried out failed to comply with the Building Regulations, whereas a civil liability might arise out of legislation such as the Defective Premises Act or the law relating to the Supply of Goods and Services.

Contractors may be liable if they carry out work designed by others which itself contravenes the statutory requirements, and often terms are included in the contract requiring the contractor to warn the employer of any defects in design of which he becomes aware.

Some forms of contract go further, and place an explicit contractual liability on the contractor. Under the JCT Standard Building Contract (clause 2.17), for example, the contractor and the contract administrator are both required to notify each other, where they become aware, of any divergence between the contract documentation or any variation and the Statutory Requirements. If the divergence concerns the documents relating to any contractor's designed portion, the contractor must inform the contract administrator of its proposed amendment for removing it. In both circumstances, the contractor must await the contract administrator's instructions.

3. The role of the Employer

Whilst most of the administration of the traditional JCT contract will be done on behalf of the employer by the contract administrator, the employer also has a role in the control of the works. This is mainly manifested in notices given to the contractor, and the issue of instructions to the contract administrator or quantity surveyor. In addition the employer has powers to carry out specific functions and may also appoint persons to carry out these functions. Figure 08-1 below highlights the key powers of the employer under the JCT Standard Building Contract. Under the JCT Design and Build Contract, where there is no reference to a contract administrator, the employer (or employer's agent) has the power to issue certain instructions specified in the contract to the contractor.

FIGURE 08-1 Key powers of the employer under the Standard Building Contract With Quantities
(Adapted from *Guide to SBC11* by Sarah Lupton, RIBA Publishing)

2·5	Defer possession of the site
2·6·1	Use or occupy the site
2·7·2	Have work executed by employer's persons
2·32	Notify the contractor of intention to deduct liquidated damages
2·33	Take possession of part of the works prior to practical completion, with contractor's consent

3·3	Appoint a representative, terminate such appointment and appoint a replacement
3·4	Appoint a clerk of works
3·8·2	Add persons to the list of sub-contractors
3·11	Employ and pay others to carry out work
4·13	Exercise right to withhold sums from monies due
6·4·3	Take out cl 6·4 insurance if contractor defaults and deduct amount from monies due
6·11·2	Terminate the contractor's employment
7·2	Assign the right to bring proceedings to any transferee
7A·1	Give notice stating that third party rights shall vest in a purchaser or tenant
7B·1	Give notice stating that third party rights shall vest in a funder
7C	Give notice requiring contractor to enter into a warranty with a purchaser or tenant
7D	Give notice requiring contractor to enter into a warranty with a funder
7E	Give notice requiring contractor to comply with requirements set out in contract particulars as to obtaining sub-contractor warranties with purchasers, tenants/funders or employer
8·4·2	Terminate the contractor's employment because of continuation of specified default
8·4·3	Terminate the contractor's employment because of repeat of specified default
8·5·1	Terminate the contractor's employment because of contractor insolvency
8·5·3·3	Take reasonable measures to ensure that the site etc. is protected
8·6	Terminate the contractor's employment because of corruption
8·7·1	Employ and pay other persons to carry out and complete the works, enter upon the site and use temporary buildings etc.
8·7·5	Pay the contractor any balance due
8·11·1	Terminate the contractor's employment because of suspension of the works
9·4·1	Give notice of arbitration
9·4·2	Give further notice of arbitration
9·7	Apply to the courts to determine a question of law
Schedule 3	
A·2	Take out and maintain a joint names policy if contractor is in default, deduct amounts payable from monies due
A·3	Inspect the contractor's policy and premium receipts or require they are sent to the CA
A·4·5	Retain amounts to cover professional fees from insurance monies

Paper 08   Contract administration: Control of the works

C·4·4	Terminate the contractor's employment by notice
C·4·4·1	Invoke the dispute resolution procedures with respect to the termination
Schedule 8	
5·1	Monitor and assess the contractor's performance by reference to any performance indicators stated or identified in the contract documents
5·3	Inform the contractor if improvement in his performance is required to meet a target for any of the specified performance indicators

3.1 The Clerk of Works

Amongst the agents the employer is entitled to employ under the traditional JCT contract is the clerk of works, to act on behalf of the employer and carry out independent inspections.

Although for traditional projects responsibility for certifying that the works are in accordance with the contract rests with the contract administrator, for large projects the contract administrator might not be able to inspect as regularly and as often as necessary, and it might therefore be appropriate for the employer to appoint a clerk of works.

The role and duties of the clerk of works are to act as an inspector under the control of the contract administrator. The clerk of works acts under the direction of the contract administrator and not as his representative. This means that any directions given by the clerk of works must be those that the contract administrator could have issued under the contract and must be confirmed in writing by the contract administrator; otherwise they will have no contractual effect. For example, if the clerk of works notifies the contractor of any work that is not in accordance with the contract, the contract administrator must confirm it.

3.2 CDM Co-ordinator

Where a project is notifiable under the Construction (Design and Management) Regulations 2007 (CDM), the employer is responsible for appointing a CDM co-ordinator and ensuring that the CDM co-ordinator's duties under the CDM regulations are carried out. A CDM co-ordinator is not required for a project which is not notifiable under the CDM regulations (i.e. a project which is not likely to involve more than 30 days, or 500 person days, of construction work or which is being carried out for a homeowner as a purely domestic project). Whilst it is the contractor's responsibility that the construction phase plan is developed to comply with the CDM regulations, the CDM co-ordinator will monitor the development of the plan.

4. The role of the Contractor

The contractor has direct control and sole responsibility for carrying out and completing the works in accordance with the contract documents. Any perceived design defects in the contract drawings must be reported, following which the contractor will await instructions from the contract administrator.

Under a traditional JCT contract, the works will normally be inspected at regular intervals by the contract administrator on behalf of the employer and, under a Design and Build contract, by the employer's agent. The contractor is required to provide reasonable access to the works, the site and the works of sub-contractors.

4.1   Person-in-charge

The contractor is required to identify and keep on site a 'person-in-charge'. To maintain the quality of workmanship required, it is important for the contractor to have an appropriately qualified person on site to supervise the work, irrespective of the type of contract being used. This person acts as the contractor's agent to receive contract administrator's instructions, clerk of works' directions and the like. If the person-in-charge is replaced, it is good practice to notify the contract administrator immediately.

For large projects there may be a team of supervisors and engineers checking that the work carried out is up to standard. This is essential if a project requires a high level of finish and fine tolerances for the main structure.

5. The role of the Contract Administrator

The contract administrator's role with respect to the employer is generally set out in a separate agreement. (See for example the JCT Consultancy Agreement.) Their role within a JCT contract will, however, be determined by the wording of the form. In a JCT Design and Build form, there is no provision for the appointment of a contract administrator, and many of the functions carried out under a traditional contract by the contract administrator will be the responsibility of the employer (who may of course employ an agent to act on his behalf).

Under the Standard Building Contract, the contract administrator is responsible for supplying information, and issuing various instructions, certificates and statements. In some cases he will act as the employer's agent, when issuing instructions for variations, for instance. In other cases he will act impartially, on issues such as extensions of time, valuation of variations, loss and expense and, for example, when issuing certificates.

The contract administrator must be given access at all reasonable times to inspect the works, and this right, in most contracts, is extended to places like the contractor's workshops and those of his sub-contractors. Access is also given to the contract administrator's representatives, including the quantity surveyor or engineer.

The purpose of the provision is mainly to check the production process, and therefore inspecting the workplace of suppliers is not included. Its purpose is to detect an issue at the earliest time so as to avoid the later use of expensive remedies, not to reduce the contractor's obligations.

6. Work, materials and goods

It is a fundamental obligation under any construction contract that the contractor must carry out and complete the works in accordance with the terms of the contract and the information provided. It therefore follows that any materials or goods supplied must be in accordance with the specification, and that contractors may be required to provide proof that materials and goods do so comply. In general, the contract documents will also specify any tests with which materials, goods or finished work are required to comply, and also normally provide for the contract administrator in traditional contracts (or employer under a Design and Build form) to order the removal from site of any work, materials or goods which do not comply.

6.1   Inspections and tests

JCT contracts allow for the issuing of instructions that require the contractor to open up for inspection any covered work, carry out tests of any materials or goods, whether incorporated into the works or not, or inspect any of the executed work. In traditional contracts such as the JCT Standard Building Contract, the inspection will typically be carried out by the contract administrator or clerk of works. Under the JCT Design and Build Contract, the inspection and testing is carried out by the employer himself or his agent.

The cost of opening up or testing, including any subsequent making good, is added to the contract sum, unless already provided for in the contract documents or unless the inspected work, materials or goods prove to be defective.

If the inspector finds on inspection that they are dissatisfied with the materials, goods or workmanship, they are required to give the reasons for their dissatisfaction to the contractor within a reasonable time from the execution of the work.

6.2   Correcting defective work

Contracts make the distinction between two types of defect:

- **Patent defects:** those that are apparent once the work, material or product is installed or completed.

- **Latent defects:** those that become apparent after a period of time, often through poor workmanship on installation.

Both need correcting, but contracts vary as to the action to be followed. Some require all defective work to be removed, whilst others allow it to be corrected in various different ways. Under the JCT Standard Building Contract, the contract administrator has powers to issue the following instructions regarding the repair of work 'not in accordance with the contract':

1. Remove from the site all or any of the defective work, materials or goods.
2. Allow the defective work, materials or goods to remain in place (after consultation with the contractor and agreement with the employer), where an appropriate

deduction from the contract sum will be made. This is used in cases where to remove the defective work may have a detrimental effect on the cost or time of the project as a whole, for instance if a considerable amount of acceptable work has already been carried out on top of the alleged defect.

3. With the agreement of the contractor, allow the defective work to remain and instruct a variation for additional works to correct the deficiency at no cost to the employer.

4. Having due regard to the Code of Practice (set out in Schedule 4 of the contract), instruct the contractor to open up and test, at his own expense, as reasonably required to establish to the satisfaction of the contract administrator 'the likelihood or extent … of any further similar non-compliance'. Where such test shows no further defects, the contractor is entitled to an extension of time, but no addition is made to the contract sum. Figure 08-2 at the end of this paper contains the Code of Practice.

Whilst the JCT Intermediate Building Contract provides essentially the same as options 1 and 3 above, it also gives the contract administrator additional powers:

- If any work is found not to be in accordance with the contract, to require the contractor to formally state within 7 days what action he proposes to take to ensure that there is no further similar failure either in work already executed or materials provided.
- If the contractor fails to make the required submission, or if the contract administrator is not satisfied with his proposals, the contract administrator can then instruct the contractor to open up any work and carry out any tests the contract administrator considers to be necessary at no cost to the employer.

The JCT Design and Build Contract provides much the same provisions as the Standard Building Contract but allowing defective work to remain unchanged is not expressly included.

6.3   Materials

JCT construction contracts require the contractor to provide materials in accordance with the specification. Where the selection of materials is by the contract administrator then the contractor has no liability for their fitness for purpose. However, the contractor's liability does extend to responsibility for hidden defects such as manufacturing defects in materials supplied.

Where choice of materials is left to the contractor, they will be required to provide materials which either meet the specified performance standards or, if no performance standards are specified, are of merchantable quality (and in addition the contractor should exercise skill and care in selecting the material).

If the specified materials become unavailable, then generally speaking, it is for the contractor to notify the contract administrator, and for the contract administrator to specify an alternative. The JCT Standard Building Contract however permits the contractor to substitute any materials, provided the contract administrator's approval is obtained.

7. Work designed by the contractor

Work designed by the contractor may comprise a contractor's designed portion, used under a traditional JCT contract, or alternatively it may be work carried out by the contractor under a JCT Design and Build contract.

Where a contractor designs work which forms part of a traditional architect-designed scheme, then the architect will be responsible for the adequacy of the performance requirements. Where work is designed on a design and build basis in response to a statement of employer's requirements, then the employer will carry responsibility for the adequacy of that document. It is therefore common for employers to employ consultant specialists to prepare the statement of employer's requirements on their behalf.

Where the employer has accepted a divergence from his requirements in the proposals submitted by the contractor, the divergence should be removed by amending the employer's requirements before the contract is executed.

As far as the work itself is concerned, the contractor has a general obligation to complete the work using materials and standards of workmanship as specified in the contract documents, usually the employer's requirements and the contractor's proposals.

In terms of quality control under the JCT Design and Build contracts, the employer employs someone to act as his agent in supervising the work to ensure that the contractor fulfils his contractual obligations. The powers exercised by the employer's agent are similar to those which would be available to a contract administrator under a traditional JCT contract.

FIGURE 08-2 Example Code of Practice for rectification of defects (JCT 2011 Standard Building Contract With Quantities)

> The purpose of the Code is to assist in the fair and reasonable operation of the requirements of clause 3·18·4.
>
> The Architect/Contract Administrator and the Contractor should endeavour to agree the amount and method of opening up or testing, but in any case, in issuing his instructions pursuant to that clause, the Architect/Contract Administrator is required to consider the following criteria:
>
> 1   the need in the event of non-compliance to demonstrate at no cost to the Employer either that it is unique and not likely to occur in similar elements of the Works or alternatively, the extent of any similar non-compliance in the Works already constructed or still to be constructed;
>
> 2   the need to discover whether any non-compliance in a primary structural element is a failure of workmanship and/or materials such that rigorous testing of similar elements must take place; or, where the non-compliance is in a less significant element, whether it is such as is to be statistically expected and can simply be repaired; or whether the non-compliance indicates an inherent weakness such as can only be found by selective testing, the extent of which must depend upon the importance of any detail concerned;
>
> 3   the significance of the non-compliance, having regard to the nature of the work in which it has occurred;
>
> 4   the consequence of any similar non-compliance on the safety of the building, its effect on users, adjoining property, the public, and compliance with any Statutory Requirements;

5 the level and standard of supervision and control of the Works by the Contractor;

6 the relevant records of the Contractor and, where relevant, those of any sub-contractor, whether resulting from the supervision and control referred to in paragraph 5 or otherwise;

7 any Codes of Practice or similar advice issued by a responsible body which are applicable to the non-compliant work, materials or goods;

8 any failure by the Contractor to carry out, or to secure the carrying out of, any tests specified in the Contract Documents or in an instruction of the Architect/Contract Administrator;

9 the reason for the non-compliance, when this has been established;

10 any technical advice that the Contractor has obtained in respect of the non-compliant work, materials or goods;

11 current recognised testing procedures;

12 the practicability of progressive testing in establishing whether any similar non-compliance is reasonably likely;

13 if alternative testing methods are available, the time required for and the consequential costs of such alternative testing methods;

14 any proposals of the Contractor; and

15 any other relevant matters.

Paper 09

Contract administration: Time

Contents

Aim

Learning outcomes

Aim

This paper aims to explain how the issue of time is dealt with under JCT forms of construction contract.

Learning outcomes

After studying this paper you should be able to:

*   Explain and comment on the contract provisions in relation to time on construction projects.
*   Discuss the roles and responsibilities of those involved in the management of time.

- Explain what actions may be taken within the contractual framework in respect of delays to the work.

1. Introduction

Time is an important factor to most clients and is often a major criterion upon which a project is assessed.

All construction projects require basic information concerning time to be included. The minimum information required is to know when a project will start and when it should be completed. As projects grow larger and more complex, much more information is needed, such as what happens if the contractor is delayed, what happens if information is not provided at the correct time, and what sanctions can be imposed by the employer if work is not completed at the proper time.

2. Commencement and possession

There are differences in construction projects between the date of commencement of the **contract** (see Paper 05 *Setting up the contract*), the date from which **works** may commence and the date upon which the contractor is permitted **access to the site**. The latter two dates may be affected by a number of factors, for example, issues relating to site ownership, access or pre-construction works by the employer.

Under the JCT range of contracts the issue is generally dealt with by including in the contract a date for possession of the site. However, the Major Project Construction Contract (the Major Project form) uses the term 'date upon which the contractor will be given access to the site' and under the Minor Works Building Contract the contractor is given the right of access to the site, not the possession of the site. There may be more than one date for possession where a project relates to construction on more than one site, or where a contractor will be allowed possession of different parts of the site at different times (this is referred to as Sections in the JCT contract). This date(s) is generally given in the tender documentation (although it may occasionally be left 'to be agreed'), and the contract requires the contractor to 'thereupon begin construction of the works ... and regularly and diligently proceed with and complete on ... Completion Date'. Generally speaking, the date(s) for possession and the date of commencement of the works are for all practical purposes the same, and other contractual provisions such as payment may be linked to this date.

Often on major construction projects, considerable work may be required by the contractor in respect of things like design, pre-construction planning and programming, prefabrication, establishment of the contractual supply chain and the mobilisation of resources before construction work actually begins on site. When using JCT contracts, this can be achieved in several ways:

- The use of a JCT Pre-Construction Services Agreement (General Contractor) between the employer and contractor facilitates many services that the contractor may carry out prior to the possession of site date and signing of the main contract. A JCT Pre-Construction Services Agreement (Specialist) can be used between the employer and the specialist for the specialist's input into the project at an early stage.
- An advance payment provision within the contract enables the employer to commission the contractor to carry out off-site works that might be desirable prior to the site possession.
- In order to enable the contractor's off-site work before the possession of the site takes place, the parties could agree an earlier due date for the first interim payment than that provided as a default position (i.e. one month after the date of possession).
- The contract could be executed well in advance of the date of possession so as to provide a proper lead-in period.

2.1 Possession and access

Timely access to the site is plainly important for construction projects, and failure by the employer to grant access by the agreed dates will have serious consequences in terms both of time and money. There is also a distinction to be made between granting possession of the site and providing a right of access. It is not unknown for the site itself to be in the employer's ownership, but for access to be dependent upon rights granted by third parties such as adjacent owners.

In most standard forms of contract there is an implied assumption that possession of the site or relevant part of the site will be exclusive to a contractor for the period of his works, and that the contractor will be responsible for site security. In some contracts the contractor may not be given the exclusive right of access and possession of the site. This may pose significant problems where multiple contractors are given simultaneous access and/or possession rights, and will require very careful drafting of the contract documents if the problems of interference between one contractor and another are to be avoided. Note also that even where exclusive possession is granted the contractor will still be required to allow access for specified others. Typical examples would be the contract administrator, persons directly employed by the employer, statutory undertakers, etc.

Under the JCT Standard Building Contract, the contractor is given the possession of the site or relevant part of the site but has an obligation to allow the employer, or other contractors working on the employer's behalf, to have access to the site and carry out other work on site where described in the contract documents, or not to withhold or delay consent to such work being carried out even when sufficient information has not been provided in advance. The contract also provides for the employer's early use of the site or the works with the contractor's consent.

2.2 Failure to grant possession and/or access by the agreed date

In the absence of any specific contractual provision, failure by the employer to grant possession and/or access by the agreed date would constitute a repudiatory breach of contract, for which the contractor would be able to either terminate the contract and sue for damages or not accept the repudiation and just claim for damages. JCT contracts therefore generally provide contractual remedies in the event that possession is delayed. In general such provisions will allow the contractor to be granted an extension of time with costs. Note, however, that an unreasonable delay may still be construed as a repudiatory breach of contract.

Under the JCT Standard Building Contract the employer may elect to reserve their right to defer possession for a period not exceeding 6 weeks or lesser period specified in the contract particulars (clause 2.5) and, if deferment occurs, an extension of time with costs would follow. Any delay in possession beyond that period would cause the employer to be in breach.

When a contract is terminated because of the employer's breach, the contractor may sue for damages. Alternatively, where a subsequent contract is renegotiated, the costs may be recovered as part of the negotiation.

3. Completion

Under most contracts, completion of the contract will be the point at which all of the parties have fulfilled their obligations to each other and the contract is therefore discharged. In the case of construction work, discharge will usually occur when the works are fully complete and the employer has paid the final bill. The parties' subsequent obligations to each other (and to any third parties to whom they may have granted rights under the contract) are then limited to those covered by the Statute of Limitations and the Latent Damages Act. Also, in a typical contract for the supply of goods, the purchaser would not take possession of the goods until they were complete, and payment would typically be made in full on delivery.

Major construction contracts, however, differ from these general arrangements in a number of ways:

- There is a need to distinguish between completion of the contract and completion of the work.
- Payment is conventionally made by instalments of various types as the work proceeds.
- The employer sometimes takes possession of the works before they are fully complete.
- The employer may take possession of the works in sections at different times.
- The employer is given the right to unilaterally change the contract works during the course of the contract and a mechanism is therefore required to change the previously agreed contractual completion date.

Given the above, a distinction must be made between the date the contract works are required to be completed, often called the date for completion, and the date work is deemed to be sufficiently complete for the employer to take possession, generally called the date of practical completion.

If the contractor has not finished the work by the required contractual completion date (the date for completion or such other date as extended under the contract), then provided the necessary contractual and statutory procedures are followed, liquidated and ascertained damages (LADs) are payable by the contractor. The amount to be deducted for liquidated damages is stated in the contract. In JCT contracts the right to deduct damages is generally subject to the issue of a non-completion certificate by the contract administrator in the traditional contracts and a non-completion notice by the employer in the Design and Build Contract.

3.1   Practical completion or substantial completion

The state of completeness is usually decided by the contract administrator or, in the design and build contract, by the employer. It is the contract administrator's opinion that determines whether the works are in a fit state to be taken over by the employer. There will inevitably be some items that are incomplete, perhaps some minor defects to be made good, but the guiding principle is whether or not the works can be safely used by the employer for the purposes for which they were designed.

The date of practical completion is important for a number of reasons, including:

- It marks the start of the rectification period.
- It marks the start of the period of final measurement.
- The first half of the retention fund is released.
- The employer takes responsibility for insuring the works.
- It marks the end of a period for which liquidated damages may be deducted.

The length of the rectification period is stated in the contract. The default position for the rectification period in the JCT contracts is 3 months for the Minor Works Building Contract and 6 months for the Standard Building Contract. During this period, minor items of work are completed and any patent defects are made good. At the end of the period an inspection is carried out and, provided that the contract administrator is satisfied, a certificate recording the making good of defects is issued. This then enables the remainder of the retention money to be released. Once the final account has been completed the final certificate may be issued.

With JCT contracts, responsibility for the completed work commonly passes to the employer immediately upon issue of the certificate of practical completion.

Note that it is a general principle that the contract administrator is required to certify practical completion as soon as, in his opinion, the works are 'practically complete'. The contract administrator in issuing a practical completion certificate would generally be governed by the common law position. A summary of the position is set out in *H. W. Neville (Sunblest) Ltd v. William Press and Son Ltd* (1981). This indicates that the work as set out in the contract documents should be complete with no patent defects. This would not necessarily mean down to the last detail, and *de minimis* works could still be outstanding.

3.2 Section completion and partial possession by the employer

Most JCT contracts permit the employer, with the agreement of the contractor, to take possession of parts of the work before practical completion of the whole. This partial possession (as distinct from sectional completion) is beneficial to the employer if he wishes to fit out the work or install specialist equipment prior to putting the building into use. The agreement of the contractor is required, but should not be unreasonably withheld. The contractor may, however, object if he can show reasonable grounds (e.g. health and safety). Assuming the contractor agrees, then the relevant parts are taken over by the employer with their own certificate of practical completion.

Note the distinction between partial possession, where the employer takes over parts of the work by agreement, and sectional completion, where the contract requires the work to be completed in specific parts, each by a specified date. In the case of sectional completion, the employer decides in advance of signing the contract that some sections of the work are to be completed by specific dates and the necessary information is included in the contract. Each identified section then has its own allocation of liquidated damages and its own section completion certificate. Note that sectional completion is a contractual obligation, but partial possession is by agreement. The contractor has no contractual obligation other than to complete the works by the stated dates.

Where a section completion certificate or a certificate confirming partial possession is issued then the general rules for practical completion apply in the case of the relevant part, in that:

- The contractor is entitled to the release of the applicable retention.
- The contractor is entitled to reduce his insurance arrangements in respect of the relevant part.
- The contractor commences the rectification period for the relevant part.
- The contractor reduces proportionately the rate of liquidated damages stated in the contract particulars.
- The contractor ceases to have any responsibility for security of the relevant part.

3.3 Acceleration

Acceleration in construction contracts is where the employer wishes to speed up the progress of the work, either to recover time lost through delays or to enable the employer to take possession of the completed building before the contractual completion date.

Not all contracts have provision for acceleration of the work to achieve early completion, and under JCT contracts the contractor is not obliged to finish early. However, in the case of the Standard Building Contract, they may agree to do so voluntarily under the acceleration quotation procedure (Schedule 2). This procedure permits the contract administrator on behalf of the employer to ask the contractor to provide an acceleration quotation. The contractor should within 21 days either provide the requested quotation which shall remain open for acceptance for not less than 7 days, or explain why early completion is impractical. The contract administrator should on behalf of the employer and within the period for acceptance confirm the acceptance of the quotation. Once the contractor has received a confirmed acceptance of his acceleration quotation the contractor is obliged to comply with its terms. Contractors are paid a reasonable sum for their preparation of the quotation if it is not accepted by the employer.

3.4 Works programme

Since virtually all construction contracts make provision for extensions of time for a variety of events, it is clear that in order to ascertain with any degree of accuracy what extensions of time are fair and reasonable the contract administrator must have some information as to the proposed rate of progress.

Most construction projects of any size therefore require the contractor to provide a programme for the construction of the work, but contracts vary in their requirements in terms of:

- The degree of detail required
- The sanctions that may be applied if the contractor fails to comply with the contractual requirements
- The contractual significance of the programme

The very basic information required by the JCT Standard Building Contract represents the lowest level of programme data. Under this contract, as soon as possible after its execution, the contractor must provide the contract administrator with his master programme, and must ensure that the programme is updated within 14 days of any revision of the completion date. The contract makes no stipulation as to the form of the programme or the degree of detail required, and provides no sanction if the contractor fails to comply with the programme except where the contractor fails to meet the respective completion date. The programming is left principally to the contractor and the contract does not seek to be prescriptive as to how the completion date should be met. If other programming information is required this can be set out in the other contract documents or by way of an amendment to the contract.

4. Postponement

There are a number of reasons why an employer may need to postpone the works in whole or in part, either before the contract has actually started or during the currency of the work, and most JCT forms of contract allow for this to take place.

- Postponement will typically give grounds for an extension of time.
- Postponement will typically give grounds for a claim for additional payment.
- Lengthy postponement may give grounds for the contractor to terminate his own employment.

It is unusual for a contractor to terminate his employment unless the project is postponed for a considerable period of time. Alternatively, if the period of delay is particularly drawn out, the contractor may wish to renegotiate the contract to allow for increases in costs.

A special case of postponement is often recognised in the finding of antiquities, and JCT forms of contract such as the Standard Building Contract and the Design and Build Contract include antiquities provisions, and the contractor is entitled to extensions of time and can claim loss and expenses in relation to finds of antiquities.

5. Extensions of time

5.1 Reasons for delay

Delays in completion of the work may occur for many reasons, but there are three basic groups:

- Delay caused by the contractor.
- Delay caused by the employer, his consultant team or his directly employed contractors.
- Delay for reasons beyond the control of either party.

Delay caused by the contractor

The contractor's primary obligation under the contract is to complete the work by the date for completion. If he fails to do so, he is in breach of contract and is therefore expected to take responsibility for the whole of the consequences of any delay caused by him and people employed and engaged by him, and to reimburse the employer for any loss incurred usually by way of liquidated damages.

Delay caused by the employer, his consultant team or his directly employed contractors

If the employer delays completion of the works (and has no right to extend time – see below), he loses the right to deduct liquidated damages because he cannot rely upon a condition that through his own fault can no longer be fulfilled.

Ways in which the employer, etc. could delay completion include:

- Delaying the starting or access dates.
- Failing to provide drawings or other information at the proper time.
- Ordering extra works that cause delay.

These are all common examples in construction work, and all of the JCT forms of contract contain provisions allowing extensions of time where the employer, etc. has caused delay. Paradoxically, the main reason for this is not to relieve contractors of their obligation to pay damages, but to protect the employer's right to deduct damages that would be lost without these powers. Without an extension of time provision time may become 'at large' and the contractor may have a reasonable time in which to finish. In the event that the contractor is then late, the employer would have to sue for damages and could not rely simply on deducting liquidated damages.

Delay for reasons beyond the control of either party

Because of the conditions under which construction works are carried out, there are often delays due to circumstances beyond the control of either the employer or the contractor. The way in which these issues are dealt with in the contract, and the extent to which they qualify for extension of time, is a function of the 'risk balance' of the contract (i.e. the way in which the risks are allocated between the employer and the contractor).

An indication of the overall risk balance of a selection of the JCT forms of contract is given in Figure 09-1. Note that because of the way in which events are described in the different forms, Figure 09-1 is not comprehensive but gives an idea of the flavour of the various different forms.

Note also that an extension of time does not automatically lead to payment for loss and expense. A separate claim is required under the clause that lists the specific causes for which loss and expense can be claimed.

FIGURE 09-1 Delays for events beyond the control of either party

Event	Standard Building Contract	Design and Build Contract	Major Project Construction Contract	Intermediate Building Contract
Exceptionally adverse weather	X	X		X
Specified perils, loss or damage	X	X	X	X
Riot, terrorism, etc.	X	X	X	X
Strikes and lockouts	X	X		X
Government action including changes in the law	X	X	X	X
Force majeure	X	X	X	X
Unanticipated shortages of labour and material				
Antiquities	X	X		
Delay by statutory undertakers or local authorities	X	X		X

5.2   *Force majeure*

Force majeure is a term that was first defined by the House of Lords in *Tennent v. Earl of Glasgow* (1864) as:

'A circumstance which no human foresight can provide against, and of which human prudence is not bound to recognise the possibility ...'

This basic 'act of God' definition has since been expanded. A statement as to its meaning in French law and confirmed for English contracts by McCardie J in *Lebeaupin v. Crispin* (1920) is:

'This term is used with reference to all circumstances independent of the will of man and which it is not in his power to control ... Thus war, inundations and epidemics are cases of force majeure; it has even been decided that a strike of workmen constitutes a case of force majeure.'

However, any contract containing a *force majeure* clause will be interpreted on the wording of the contract.

In building contracts using a JCT form the meaning is restricted, since some matters which could be construed as falling within its definition are mentioned in their own right (e.g. extremely adverse weather conditions, acts of terrorism, strikes).

Force majeure clauses basically limit the contractor's risk by removing his liability to pay damages for late completion if a *force majeure* event should occur. If this clause were omitted, then in certain circumstances the courts might hold that events could occur that would make it impossible for one party to meet its obligations through no fault of either party. In these circumstances it would be inequitable effectively to hold that party liable for any losses suffered by the other. The contract might therefore be regarded as frustrated. Note that in this case the contract would come to an end, which on large-scale contracts is the last thing the employer would want.

The situation may, however, be only temporary, and the employer may wish to keep the contract alive. This can be accomplished by the inclusion of a suitable *force majeure* clause. Under such a clause the basic principles are usually as follows:

- The party prevented from continuing will receive an extension of time.
- Neither party will have a financial claim against the other (i.e. each party will bear its own costs).
- The contract remains in force and all other obligations remain unaffected.

5.3 Processes and procedures

All construction contracts will set out processes and procedures for the assessment of extension of time claims. In general the assessment will be made by the contract administrator following notification of the delay event by the contractor, and in most cases contract administrators will be required to allocate specific extensions of time to specific events. Contracts will typically provide a timeframe within which the contract administrator must act and, since the employer's right to deduct liquidated damages has historically been considered to be dependent upon all relevant contractual procedures being properly

complied with, timely and accurate compliance has been considered to be essential (*Peak Construction v. McKinney Foundations* (1970)).

The various different forms adopt different approaches to the extension of time process. The process set out in the JCT 2011 Standard Building Contract is as follows:

- Contractor notifies delay 'if and whenever it becomes reasonably apparent that the progress of the works ... is being or is likely to be delayed', giving the cause(s) of the delay.
- Contract administrator decides whether the events qualify for extension of time, and whether the completion of the work is likely to be delayed beyond the completion date. He must issue the relevant notice as soon as reasonably practicable and in any event within 12 weeks of receipt of the contractor's notification.
- This process is repeated each time there is a delay.
- Following practical completion the contract administrator may, within a further period of 12 weeks, review all extensions of time granted and may adjust the overall contract completion date if he considers it fair and reasonable to do so.

Similar provisions are included in the JCT Intermediate Building Contract, the JCT Design and Build Contract and the JCT Major Project Construction Contract, although there are differences in the period of time within which the contract administrator (or in the latter two forms, the employer) is required to act.

Paper 10

Contract administration: Termination and insolvency

Contents

Aim

Learning outcomes

1. **Introduction**
   1.1 Termination by the employer
   1.2 Termination by the contractor
   1.3 Termination by either party

2. **Insolvency**
   2.1 Insolvency of the contractor under JCT contracts
   2.2 Insolvency of the employer under JCT contracts

3. **Administration**

4. **Effect on construction contracts**

Aim

This paper aims to introduce the basic principles of dealing with a JCT construction contract where the project is required to be terminated.

Learning outcomes

After studying this paper you should be able to:

- Understand why and how termination occurs
- Understand the procedures for terminating a contract under a JCT contract
- Understand the different types of insolvency
- Identify the signs leading to insolvency
- Prepare a procedure to deal with contract continuation
- Describe the special contractual problems on continuation contracts

1. Introduction

Most forms of contract used in the construction industry contain provisions to allow termination of the project before the works are complete. Under JCT contracts, termination can be initiated by either the employer or the contractor, depending on the circumstances. Termination is set out in section 8 of the JCT Standard Building Contract 2011 (SBC) and the JCT Design and Build Contract 2011 (DB) and, insofar as relevant, contains standard provisions across the JCT suite of contracts. Note the distinction between termination of the contractor's employment provided for under JCT contracts (referred to later) and that of termination of the contract. If termination is considered then the procedure set out in the contract should be followed, notwithstanding that under SBC 2011 and DB 2011 the employer's and contractor's rights of termination for default or insolvency are without prejudice to any other rights and remedies they may have.

1.1   Termination by the employer

It is generally one of two factors that leads an employer to terminate the contractor's employment. First, a default by the contractor, where the contractor fails in one or more of their obligations resulting in a breach of contract, or second, where the contractor becomes insolvent.

The types of default covered within JCT contracts generally include:

- Suspending the carrying out of the work for no valid reason.
- Failing to proceed regularly and diligently with the works.
- Failure to comply with instructions in connection with defective work, materials or goods.
- Failure to comply with clauses dealing with assignments/sub-contracting of work.
- Failure to comply with the CDM Regulations.

The termination of the contractor's employment is a drastic step to take and should not be taken without careful thought and consultation.

It is common in most forms of contract to give the contractor a warning and allow him the opportunity to rectify the situation. Where termination is sought the contract administrator (SBC) or employer (DB) is first required to issue a notice of default giving details of the default. If the contractor continues the default for 14 days from receipt of notice, the employer then has 21 days from the expiry of that 14 day period to issue the termination notice.

The issue of a notice of **default** is generally a prerequisite to the issue of a notice of **termination**, and if this procedure is not followed the termination is invalid and the contractor may claim damages for breach of contract.

In the event of the contractor becoming insolvent it is not necessary to issue a **default** notice and a **termination** notice can be issued directly.

1.2 Termination by the contractor

Similarly, in the case of termination by the contractor, a termination occurs most commonly through default or insolvency on the part of the employer. The types of default covered within JCT contracts include:

- Not paying by the final date the full amount due to the contractor for an interim payment.
- Interfering with or obstructing the issue of any certificate under the contract (SBC).
- Failing to comply with the terms of assignment under the contract.
- Failing to comply with CDM Regulations.

In addition, termination by the contractor may also be brought about if, before practical completion, the works are suspended for a specified reason for a continuous period of the length stated in the contract particulars (this is 2 months unless some other period is stated). The specified reasons are:

- The contractor is waiting for instructions from the contract administrator in relation to any discrepancy highlighted in the contract documents, or instructions relating to variations or postponement of the works.
- There is an impediment, prevention or default preventing the continuation of the works, whether by act or omission, by the employer, contract administrator, quantity surveyor, or any of the 'employer's persons'.

If the default continues for 14 days from the receipt of notice, then the contractor may, on or within 21 days from the expiry of the 14 day period, terminate his employment under the contract.

1.3 Termination by either party

In some instances termination of a contract may be initiated by either party. Under JCT contracts this can arise because, prior to completion of the works, the project has been suspended for the relevant continuous period stated in the contract particulars (as stated before), this is 2 months unless some other period is stated) for reasons of:

- *Force majeure.*
- Instructions issued by the contract administrator as a result of negligence or default by any Statutory Undertaker.
- Loss or damage to the works as a result of the Specified Perils (the contractor is not permitted to give notice of termination here, if the cause of the damage was initiated by his own negligence or default).
- Civil commotion, the use or threat of terrorism, and the activities of the relevant authorities in dealing with the event of such threat.
- Any exercise of a statutory power by the UK Government that directly affects the execution of the works.

Either party, if the suspension of the works continues for longer than the 7 day period after notice has been given, may then terminate the contractor's employment by giving a notice to that effect.

A similar process as outlined below in 2.2 (*Insolvency of the employer under JCT contracts*) must then take place. The contractor will prepare an account or, at the employer's option, provide the documentation necessary for the employer to do so, to determine the costs payable to both parties as a result of the termination. The employer shall pay the contractor (or vice versa) the amount payable in respect of the account within 28 days of its submission to the other party, without deduction of any retention.

2. Insolvency

Insolvency is a generic term, covering both individuals and companies. Bankruptcy applies specifically to the insolvency of individuals; liquidation specifically to the insolvency of companies.

Insolvency is an ongoing problem with the construction industry traditionally appearing high in the table of number of failures each year. In order to appreciate the reasons for this, one must understand how the industry functions.

- **Structure of industry.** There is a very large number of small firms within the industry and only a small number (around 80) of organisations that could be described as large. However, even many of these large organisations would be considered small in comparison with other industries.

  There are good reasons for this. A large volume of work is of the repairs and maintenance type and often small in value, requiring the use of smaller firms to carry out this work.

- **The way firms are set up.** It is very easy to set up in business as a building contractor or sub-contractor, and at present there is no legal requirement to employ people with any business or technical expertise. Most plant will be hired and materials often obtained on credit. With interim payment provisions available, it is therefore possible to operate from a very limited capital base, and a high proportion of the problems occur through lack of administrative knowledge and insufficient capital, rather than deficiencies of a technical nature.

- **How work is obtained.** Firms bid for work in competition with other contractors, often quoting a fixed price for a long duration, using in many instances sub-contract quotations which may be withdrawn after main contract commencement but before a sub-contract is entered into.

  The costs are based on historic labour and plant outputs which may or may not be achieved on site, with a lot of this work being done outside and subject to the vagaries of climate.

- **Stop-Go demand for work.** It is generally impossible for contractors to produce an accurate business plan which includes projection of future workloads. Government and semi-government clients account for a high proportion of the industry's output and any cut-back or expansion of capital expenditure will have a significant effect upon demand. When taken in conjunction with fiscal measures, therefore, this will have a considerable effect upon private demand.

It can be seen, therefore, that because of the uncertainty of demand, contractors/investors are going to be loath to invest large amounts of capital with such an uncertain outcome unless they have confidence in the future market.

The rules governing the administration of both corporate and individual insolvency are contained in the Insolvency Act 1986 (as amended). In bankruptcy, the bankrupt's property vests in the 'trustee in bankruptcy'; in liquidation, the company's property passes to the control of the 'liquidator'.

The JCT Standard Building Contract provides a definition of insolvency in terms of the Insolvency Act 1986. (See Figure 10-1.) It is this definition that is important because any event that is so defined will be the trigger that allows the other party to operate the termination provisions of the contract.

FIGURE 10-1 Meaning of insolvency under the Standard Building Contract

Meaning of insolvency

8·1   For the purposes of these Conditions:

    ·1   a Party which is a company becomes Insolvent:

        ·1   when it enters administration within the meaning of Schedule B1 to the Insolvency Act 1986;

        ·2   on the appointment of an administrative receiver or a receiver or manager of its property under Chapter I of Part III of that Act, or the appointment of a receiver under Chapter II of that Part;

        ·3   on the passing of a resolution for voluntary winding-up without a declaration of solvency under section 89 of that Act; or

        ·4   on the making of a winding-up order under Part IV or V of that Act.

    ·2   a Party which is a partnership becomes Insolvent:

        ·1   on the making of a winding-up order against it under any provision of the Insolvency Act 1986 as applied by an order under section 420 of that Act; or

        ·2   when sequestration is awarded on the estate of the partnership under section 12 of the Bankruptcy (Scotland) Act 1985 or the partnership grants a trust deed for its creditors.

    ·3   a Party who is an individual becomes Insolvent:

        ·1   on the making of a bankruptcy order against him under Part IX of the Insolvency Act 1986; or

        ·2   on the sequestration of his estate under the Bankruptcy (Scotland) Act 1985 or when he grants a trust deed for his creditors.

Paper 10   Contract administration: Termination and insolvency

·4   a Party also becomes Insolvent if:

 ·1   he enters into an arrangement, compromise or composition in satisfaction of his debts (excluding a scheme of arrangement as a solvent company for the purposes of amalgamation or reconstruction); or

 ·2   (in the case of a Party which is a partnership) each partner is the subject of an individual arrangement or any other event or proceedings referred to in this clause 8·1.

Each of clauses 8·1·1 to 8·1·4 also includes any analogous arrangement, event or proceedings in any other jurisdiction.

Many of the rules relating to insolvency are common to both bankruptcy and liquidation. However, there are several important differences, which are designed to reflect:

- In the case of bankruptcy, the societal role of the family unit and the function of the matrimonial home.
- In the case of liquidation, the importance of limited liability.

The majority of construction work, of course, is carried out by companies.

Where there are no express rules in the contract, insolvency as such would give the employer no right of termination. The trustee in bankruptcy or the liquidator, as the case may be, has the right to complete the contract if it will be to the benefit of the estate, or to disclaim the contract if completion is likely to be unprofitable. If, as a result of the insolvency, the contractor is unable to obtain materials to carry out the works so that ultimately the work comes to a stop, it would amount to common law repudiation and the employer could then treat the contract as at an end. However, this would result from the stoppage of work and not from the insolvency.

In order to protect the interests of the employer, JCT contracts contain provisions to regulate the position in the event of insolvency, including the right to bring the contractor's employment to an end. Although the general law permits the parties to arrange that upon bankruptcy or liquidation of the contractor, either the contractor's employment may be terminated or the contract as a whole may be brought to an end, JCT contracts specifically provide for the former. This maintains the contract and keeps alive many of the other provisions; this provides the employer with greater freedom and without necessarily having to make a claim through the courts. Where either party wishes to terminate the contract as a whole, advice should always be taken about the operation of such provisions and how to proceed.

2.1   Insolvency of the contractor under JCT contracts

In the event that the contractor becomes insolvent, the employer may terminate the contractor's employment at any time by providing notice. The contractor must notify the employer immediately of any proposal, meeting or proceedings relating to his insolvency e.g. appointment of an administrator, voluntary winding-up, or being subject to a winding-up order.

Where the contractor's employment is terminated, his obligations to carry out and complete the works under the contract are suspended and the employer may take measures to ensure that the site, the works, and site materials are adequately protected and the materials remain on site. The contractor is obliged to allow the employer to carry out these measures. The employer may employ others to carry out and complete the works and (subject to any third-party consents) may take possession of the site, and may use any existing temporary buildings, plant, tools, equipment and site materials to complete the project.

The contractor is required (when notified in writing by the contract administrator) to remove from the works any of their temporary buildings, plant, tools, equipment or goods. In addition, in SBC (where there is contractor's design) and DB, the contractor must, without charge, provide the employer with copies of the Contractor's Design Documents. The contractor may also be required to assign to the employer (without charge) the benefit of any agreement in place for the supply of services or goods for the purpose of carrying out the works.

2.2   Insolvency of the employer under JCT contracts

In the event that the employer becomes insolvent, the contractor, by written notice, can terminate his own employment under the contract. The employer must notify the contractor of any proposal, meeting or proceedings relating to his insolvency. The contractor's obligations to carry out and complete the works under the contract are then suspended.

Upon termination of the contractor's employment, the contractor must, as soon as is reasonably possible, prepare and submit an account to the employer covering the following amounts:

- The total value of the work properly executed at the date of termination, ascertained in accordance with the conditions of the contract as if the employment had not been terminated, together with any amounts due to the contractor under the conditions.
- Any sums ascertained in respect of direct loss and/or expense with regard to matters affecting regular progress under clause 4.23.
- Cost of removal of temporary buildings, plant, tools, equipment, goods or equipment.
- The cost of materials or goods (including site materials) properly ordered for the works for which the contractor has then paid or is legally bound to pay.
- Any direct loss and/or damage caused to the contractor by the termination.

After taking into account the amounts previously paid to the contractor, the employer must pay the contractor (or vice versa) the amount properly due in respect of the account within 28 days of its submission.

3. Administration

Administration was first introduced in the Insolvency Act 1986 with the purpose of attempting to rescue a company so that it may survive as a going concern, or in order to maximise the assets of the company.

Once the company has gone into liquidation, an administration order cannot be made. However, prior to this the courts can make such an order where it thinks that the following might be achieved:

- The survival of the company
- A more advantageous realisation of the assets
- A compromise between the company and its creditors

Once an order has been issued, in principle no liquidation or winding-up procedures may be initiated. Therefore, in effect, it gives the company breathing space to consider the options. Whilst the order is in force, the administrator will run the business.

Because JCT contracts generally provide for the right to terminate the contractor's employment upon insolvency which includes entering into administration, the employer is able to either continue the contract with the contractor in administration or to terminate and get the work done by others.

4. Effect on construction contracts

Great care should be taken when placing main and sub-contracts to choose the contractors carefully. Full technical and financial pre-selection procedures should be carried out for all contractors prior to tendering. (See Paper 02 *Contractor selection and tendering*.)

However, even with careful screening, problems can occur. The benefits of carefully prepared contract documentation with inbuilt client safeguards are important.

There are many practical effects on a building contract that arise when the main contractor has financial problems. The situation can be divided into the following stages:

- First signs
- Twilight time
- Insolvency
- Immediate tasks
- Financial appraisal
- Completion
- The final account

First signs

Before a contractor becomes insolvent, there are often signs that all is not well. It is important to be vigilant and, if any of these signs appear, to be extremely careful in all dealings under the contract and above all not to instigate any precipitate action which might later leave the employer exposed to claims for breach of contract.

Things to look for:

- **Sub-contractors:** Often one of the first signs is non-payment of sub-contractors, although this is not an infallible guide.
- **Interim payments:** Requests for earlier payments than normal, or faster processing, or collecting payment by hand.
- **Progress of work:** A reduction in the amount of work done and/or reduced labour force.
- **Materials:** A reduction in the amount of materials being delivered or in some instances unauthorised removal of materials often by sub-contractors.
- **Staffing:** Frequent staff changes and unusual site visitors, e.g. head office personnel. Beware any strange visitors visiting the site with clipboards. They may be quantity surveyors employed by a bank and put in to check on work progress and value. This could be a prelude to the bank appointing a receiver or perhaps putting together a rescue package.

Twilight time

As mentioned above, great care must be taken during these difficult times. Each interim valuation may turn out to be the last. Scrupulous adherence to the conditions of contract is recommended, and interim certificates should be paid by the dates required under the contract. However, any safety measures that can be made should be taken.

- Requests to remove materials should be resisted.
- A check should be made to make sure all insurances are in place and up-to-date.
- Follow proof of payment procedures.
- Discuss with the contract administrator the situation regarding defective work.

Insolvency

This usually happens very quickly. One minute the contractor is trading and the next an administrator or liquidator has officially been put in. Once the contractor is insolvent as defined in clause 8.1, the termination process can be commenced.

Immediate tasks

A number of issues must be resolved following termination but some tasks are more urgent than others. Some of these urgent tasks may include:

- **Stop payment:** Once the contractor's employment is terminated then there is no requirement to make further payment, including in certain situations any sum already due, until the project has been completed.
- **Site security:** It is essential to provide a secure site so that an accurate assessment of the employer's position can be made. This may involve erecting security fencing and gates and supplying security checks on site on a 24-hour basis if appropriate.
- **Check contract provisions:** Has a bond been used? Keep bond-holder informed to save problems later.

- Take steps to maintain essential services to the site.
- **Liquidation:** Check liquidator accepts termination and keep informed.
- **Protection:** Make sure new insurances are in place.
  If necessary protect works from damage and consider any health and safety matters.

Other tasks:

- **Work schedule:** Produce a schedule of the work, stating the amount of work done and identifying any defective work.
- **Photographic records:** It is advisable to prepare photographic evidence of the state of the contract at the time of the termination, because once the completion work commences it would not be possible to identify what had been done.
- **As-built drawings:** A set of drawings should be kept showing the extent of the work completed satisfactorily.
- **Financial control:** A control procedure should be set up to record staff costs incurred due to the insolvency. Any additional fees will be charged against the contractor. Comprehensive back-up records will therefore be necessary to substantiate the amount.

Financial appraisal

At this point a complete financial appraisal of the project is necessary, covering the following:

- **Work done:** From the work schedule it will be possible to calculate the value of the work properly executed.
- **Materials:** It will be necessary to produce a complete list of materials on site. Once this list has been produced then it will be essential to establish ownership of the materials.
- **Plant:** As with materials, a plant schedule should be prepared and then ownership of the plant agreed.
- **Temporary works:** Again, a schedule of temporary works must be made, the legal position being the same as for plant. Any contractor-owned items can be retained in order to obtain completion.

Completion

The main objective should be to complete the project as early as possible. Delay will cost money which may not be able to be recovered in full from the contractor.

There is no restriction on the way that the completion of the work is arranged. However, it is good practice to keep the administrator/liquidator and bond-holder (if there is one) informed. However one should bear in mind that there is always a common law duty to mitigate one's loss.

It may be reasonable to consider letting a small contract to basically tidy up the site by way of doing work to bring the project to an easily identifiable break point and to prepare site for a new contract. This could well prove beneficial later, as the management and control of the site, particularly in the later stages, is unlikely to have been of the highest order.

This work can be done whilst a new procurement route is being carried out for the completion contract, so could well save time overall.

There are four basic approaches to arranging for completion of the work:

- Reinstatement
- Assignment
- Novation
- Arranging separate completion

The method adopted to arrange completion may largely depend on the stage that the project has reached prior to the termination.

Where the contract is near completion, reinstatement of the original contract may be the best approach for both parties – see clause 8.3.2 for specific reference to this option. However, if this is not possible then it may be feasible to let direct packages of work often to the original sub-contractors. In certain circumstances the quickest approach may be a cost reimbursement type arrangement. Where a large amount of work is left to be completed, then other approaches would need to be considered.

It may be possible to negotiate a value with the original second lowest contractor and thereby save time. However, the current economic climate would of course have to be taken into account when agreeing a price.

Where competitive tendering is considered to be the best option it is usually possible to use the original project documentation as the basis for the tender process. There are, however, special circumstances for this type of work that would need to be brought to the tenderer's notice in the documents:

- Incorporate schedule of condition of works
- Incorporate photographs
- List available materials
- Describe plant available
- Describe temporary works available

In deciding what documentation to use, one should bear in mind the final account procedure and the need to be able to calculate all parties' rights and liabilities and produce a set of documents to aid this process.

The final account

A number of accounts will be necessary in this type of situation.

It will be necessary to calculate the actual cost to the employer, taking into account the value of the first contractor's work together with the completion contract, and also taking into account any additional costs arising out of the insolvency.

It is also necessary to calculate how much it would have cost the employer to obtain his project had the insolvency not occurred.

At the end of the calculation, any surplus/shortfall will require payment or recovery by the employer.

Any money owed to the original contractor can be used to offset any debt due to costs incurred by the employer. This set-off will be based on mutual dealings provided that the same organisations are involved.

Paper 11

Introduction to dispute resolution

Contents

Aim

Learning outcomes

1. **Introduction**

2. **The ADR hierarchy**

3. **Dispute resolution in construction contracts**

4. **Adjudication under the Scheme for Construction Contracts**
   4.1 Procedure
   4.2 Powers and duties of the adjudicator
   4.3 Powers and duties of the parties
   4.4 The decision
   4.5 The effects of the decision

5. **Dispute resolution under the JCT contracts**
   5.1 Negotiation
   5.2 Mediation
   5.3 Adjudication
   5.4 Arbitration
   5.5 Litigation

Aim

The aim of this paper is to provide an introduction to methods of dispute resolution in JCT construction contracts.

Learning outcomes

After studying this paper, you should be able to:

- Describe the major methods of dispute resolution in common use.
- Explain the dispute resolution requirements of the Scheme for Construction Contracts.

Introduction to dispute resolution

- Comment upon the effectiveness of adjudication as a means of solving disputes on construction contracts.
- Explain the dispute resolution procedures of the JCT 2011 Standard Building Contract.

1. Introduction

In principle, save for the right to adjudication under the Construction Act, the parties to any dispute are free to choose their own method of resolving it. The two approaches traditionally used in construction contracts are litigation and arbitration. Arbitration is governed by the Arbitration Act 1996.

The difficulty with both litigation and arbitration is that they are costly and time-consuming, and in some cases can only be started after the contract has either been completed or completely broken down. In addition, a judgement of the court, or an award by an arbitrator, is frequently obtained only years after the contract has been completed or abandoned.

There has therefore long been a view that the conventional dispute resolution approaches did not adequately meet the needs of the parties. This was particularly evident in the case of complex contracts such as those for construction, and in those where the relationships between people were of predominant importance for example in family law. It was quickly realised that, in cases such as these, many potential disputes could be avoided if the parties could be helped to resolve their differences before the split became catastrophic. There was plainly a need for dispute resolution techniques which were timely, had an element of informality, and could be brought quickly into play.

Accordingly a body of 'alternative dispute resolution' (ADR) techniques has been developed to meet this need.

2. The ADR hierarchy

A wide variety of ADR procedures and techniques has been developed, but the following brief hierarchy illustrates the principal variations.

Mediation

Here the mediator is appointed to facilitate the parties in resolving their dispute. Mediators are typically appointed when disputes or differences that arise under the contract cannot be solved, in the first instance, by direct negotiation between the contracting parties. Note that:

- The mediator takes no active part in the negotiation itself: their role is limited to that of non-judgemental facilitator.

- Since it is the parties who are resolving their own dispute, there is no reason for them to be bound by the precise terms of the contract, merely that they should reach some agreement.

Mediation is becoming increasingly popular as a means of resolving construction disputes, particularly when the contract is based on a collaborative approach.

Conciliation

Here the conciliator attempts to assist the parties to reach agreement, perhaps by helping them each to present their point of view or by advising them as to possible courses of action. Note again that the process is non-judgemental. It is not part of the conciliator's role to decide upon the rights and wrongs of the case, his role is simply to promote agreement.

Adjudication

Here the adjudicator forms an opinion upon the rights and wrongs of the case, based upon evidence presented to him and his own investigations. The adjudicator's decision is binding on the parties and has legal effect until finally determined by legal proceedings, by arbitration or by agreement between the parties.

3. Dispute resolution in construction contracts

More so than most contracts, to be effective and successful, construction contracts need the goodwill of the parties and a spirit of co-operation. These qualities can soon be lost or soured if a dispute arises between the parties during the contract works; particularly since they know that it is unlikely to be resolved for a considerable period and at the expense of legal costs and lost management time.

Further, the dispute may hinder the progress of the work itself. In an extreme example, though sadly all too common in the construction industry, the withholding of payment over disputed items has led to the insolvency of a party, which inevitably led to delay and increased costs. The question was: how to minimise the number of disputes and, if and when they do arise, how to manage them in the most effective way.

What was needed was a quicker method of resolving disputes arising during contract work that could be either accepted as final or reopened in litigation or arbitration if either party still felt aggrieved. Sir Michael Latham, in his report *Constructing the Team* in July 1994, recognised the difficulty. He considered a number of dispute resolution methods, such as mediation, conciliation and multi-tiered ADR, but having held wide consultation within the industry, he determined that adjudication should be the normal method of dispute resolution.

4. Adjudication under the Scheme for Construction Contracts

4.1 Procedure

- **Notice of adjudication**
  A notice setting out details of the dispute must be given to every other party to the contract by the party requiring adjudication ('the referring party').

- **Appointment of adjudicator**
  The parties may agree upon an adjudicator or have already named an adjudicator in the contract. Alternatively, the contract may have specified a nominating body, or the referring party may approach an adjudicator-nominating body, which must identify an appropriate adjudicator within 5 days.

  If the adjudicator is unwilling or unable to act, they must tell the parties within 2 days. If prepared to act, they must declare any interest in any matter relating to the dispute. A request to act as adjudicator must be accompanied by a copy of the notice of adjudication. The objection of any party to a particular adjudicator does not invalidate their appointment or decision.

- **Referral notice**
  Within 7 days of the notice of adjudication, the referring party must refer the dispute in writing to the adjudicator, together with copies of the contract (or relevant extracts from it) and other relevant documents on which they intend to rely. They must also copy the documents to other parties to the dispute.

- **Other disputes**
  With the consent of the parties, the adjudicator may adjudicate on more than one dispute under the same contract and on related disputes under different contracts.

- **Resignation of adjudicator**
  The adjudicator may resign by notice in writing to the parties. They must resign if they find the dispute has already been adjudicated.

- **Revocation of appointment**
  The parties may agree to revoke the adjudicator's appointment at any time. They will be liable for fees and expenses unless the revocation is due to the default or misconduct of the adjudicator.

4.2 Powers and duties of the adjudicator

The basic duty of the adjudicator is to act impartially and make a decision in accordance with the terms of the contract and the relevant law, while at the same time avoiding unnecessary expense. They are given very wide powers to investigate the dispute (as opposed to making his decision simply based upon what representations the parties choose to put before him).

They may take the initiative in ascertaining both facts and law and decide on the procedure to be adopted in the adjudication.

The adjudicator may:

- require documents to be produced, including written statements, representations and submissions from any party;
- decide the language of the adjudication and whether any translations are necessary;
- meet and question the parties;
- make site visits;
- carry out tests and experiments;
- with the knowledge of the parties' appointed experts, assessors or legal advisers, give directions relating to the conduct of the adjudication, including a timetable and deadlines;
- limit the length of written or oral submissions.

4.3 Powers and duties of the parties

The parties are under a duty to comply with any request or direction of the adjudicator. If they do not, the adjudicator may continue the adjudication in the absence of the defaulting party and/or in the absence of any documentation that he may have requested and has not been produced. The adjudicator may draw such inferences as are justified by a party's default. He may attach such weight as he thinks fit to information produced out of time.

The parties may be represented, such representation being limited to one person only when the adjudicator is hearing oral evidence or representations, unless the adjudicator decides otherwise.

Neither the parties nor the adjudicator may disclose any confidential information or documentation relating to the adjudication.

4.4 The decision

The adjudicator shall reach his decision not later than:

- 28 days after receipt of the referral notice; or
- 42 days after receipt of the referral notice if the referring party consents; or
- a longer period if all parties agree.

They must deliver a copy of the decision to each of the parties to the contract. In their decision they may:

- open up, revise and review any decision or certificate not expressed in the contract to be final and conclusive;
- decide that a party is liable to make a payment, and state when it falls due and the final date for payment;

- if the contract provides for payment of interest, decide the circumstances in which and the rate at which simple or compound interest shall be paid.

If requested by any party to the dispute, the adjudicator shall provide reasons for their decision.

4.5 The effects of the decision

Unless otherwise directed, the parties shall comply with the decision immediately. The decision is binding until the dispute is finally determined by litigation, arbitration or agreement. The parties may treat the adjudicator's decision as final. There is no procedure in the Scheme to enable a party to appeal against the adjudicator's decision.

The court may enforce any peremptory order made by the adjudicator:

- at their request; or
- at the request of a party with the adjudicator's permission; or
- with the agreement of the parties.

The adjudicator is entitled to payment of their reasonable fees and expenses and, subject to any contractual provision that complies with section 108A(2) of the Construction Act, the adjudicator may determine how these are to be apportioned. The parties are jointly and severally liable for any sum which remains outstanding following the making of any such determination. The adjudicator cannot be sued unless his act or omission is in bad faith.

5. Dispute resolution under the JCT contracts

The JCT contracts generally contain provisions in relation to five means of settling disputes:

5.1 Negotiation

With a view to avoidance or early resolution of actual or potential disputes, each party should notify disputes promptly and nominate an employee of sufficient seniority and authority in order to resolve them quickly by direct, good faith negotiations.

5.2 Mediation

If disputes or differences arise under the contract that the parties are unable to solve by direct negotiations, they may, by agreement, seek to resolve disputes through mediation.

5.3 Adjudication

The parties have a contractual right as well as the statutory right to refer disputes to adjudication, with the adjudication being conducted in accordance with the Scheme for Construction Contracts, subject to the following further provisions:

- For the purposes of the Scheme, the adjudicator may be named and the nominating body identified in the contract particulars.
- Where the dispute relates to opening up and testing for other non-compliant work (clause 3.18.4):
    - The appointed adjudicator must be an individual with appropriate expertise and experience in the specialist area or discipline relevant to the dispute.
    - If the adjudicator does not have the appropriate expertise, they shall appoint an independent expert to advise and report in writing whether or not the instruction issued under clause 3.18.4 is reasonable in all the circumstances.

5.4   Arbitration

If arbitration is required, the parties need to take positive action in the contract particulars or by later making an arbitration agreement, otherwise litigation is the final forum for resolving any disputes. The contract particulars provide the option of agreeing to refer disputes to arbitration by making the appropriate entry. The arbitration agreement is subject to the three exceptions set out in the contract (Article 8 in SBC 2011) and arbitration is to be conducted in accordance with the arbitration clauses (9.3 to 9.8 in SBC 2011) and the JCT 2011 edition of the Construction Industry Model Arbitration Rules (CIMAR) (http://www.jctltd.co.uk/docs/JCT_CIMAR_2011.pdf).

Exceptions are:

- Either party has a right to refer any disputes to adjudication.
- Any disputes arising under the Construction Industry Scheme or VAT legislation, if that legislation provides another dispute resolution method.
- Any disputes in connection with enforcement of an Adjudicator's decision.

5.5   Litigation

Subject to adjudication and (where applicable) arbitration, the contract records the jurisdiction of the English courts; selection of another jurisdiction requires an appropriate amendment.